TOUCH, TICKLE and PAIN
PART TWO

A cartoon by the famous cartoonist, Lundquist, in *Dagens Nyheter*, one of Sweden's leading newspapers, on 3rd May 1945, the day after the title of Professor was conferred on me by the Government. A free translation of the rhyme which accompanied it is given below:

> This is Gulle Yngve Zotterman. He
> Is a wizard at physiology.
> He knows the way that nerves transmit,
> With the title of Professor he'll now sit,
> He knows how thoughts come to the brain –
> A doctor not easily matched again.
> So raise your hat in the street. Salute
> This Reader of Karolinska Institute.

TOUCH, TICKLE and PAIN

PART TWO

BY

YNGVE ZOTTERMAN
M.D., V.M.D. Holm., D.V.M. Bern., Sc.D. Cantab.

PERGAMON PRESS

OXFORD - NEW YORK - TORONTO
SYDNEY - BRAUNSCHWEIG

Pergamon Press Ltd., Headington Hill Hall, Oxford
Pergamon Press Inc., Maxwell House, Fairview Park, Elmsford,
New York 10523
Pergamon of Canada Ltd., 207 Queen's Quay West, Toronto 1
Pergamon Press(Aust.) Pty. Ltd., 19a Boundary Street,
Rushcutters Bay, N.S.W. 2011, Australia
Vieweg & Sohn GmbH, Burgplatz 1, Braunschweig

First edition 1971

Library of Congress Catalog Card No. 70-91702

Printed in Sweden by Vadstena Affärstryck

08 016052 2

Contents

Foreword

It is said that anybody can write an interesting story about their childhood and most people enjoy making nostalgic excursions back to the days of their youth. For that reason it is perhaps dangerous to write about one's own adult life as I have done in this volume, which contains some of my experiences from 1927 to 1969. During this period there has been an enormous development in my particular field of scientific research, neurophysiology. To a great extent this has been due to an equally extraordinary revolution in electronic engineering, which has enabled those of us who work in the field of sensory physiology to bridge the gap when we experience a conscious sensation between the external event taking place in the peripheral sense organ and the physical reaction in the cerebral cortex.

This technical progress is reflected in all kinds of human endeavours today, and has resulted in gradual but basic changes in man's condition on our planet. For this reason it may be of some interest to give a worm's-eye view of this progress in my reminiscences of forty years of the twentieth century. I must emphasize that they are truly reminiscences, for I have never kept a diary, except for the four months in 1940 that I spent in the U.S.A.

This book gives, of course, only brief glimpses of my activities after I returned to Sweden from two years in England. I have tried to tell the story of a young scientist's struggle in a period of incredibly rapid advances. After two years of research with three of Britain's most outstanding life scientists (E. D. Adrian,

Thomas Lewis and A. V. Hill) and the advantages this gave me, I was left to build up my own research by personal effort alone. It was a struggle; it took a long time; it was painful in every meaning of the word. I was sometimes advised to give it all up and go into medical practice. I did not follow that advice, partly because for nearly fifteen years I used to spend my long vacations (three months each year) with the Swedish Navy. But this naval service led me into applied naval physiology, as well as into industrial physiology. During World War II I spent long periods investigating the conditions of lumberjacks in the deep forests of Wermland. At the end of that war I was fortunate in being appointed head of the department of physiology at the Veterinary College in Stockholm, and this gave me excellent opportunities for extending my research into sensory physiology. I received much support from my veterinary colleagues and from the Government. I had the good fortune to be joined by brilliant young veterinarians who are today expert physiologists with worldwide reputations. Thus my life has had its struggle and pain, but it has also had its rewards! The best of these are all the friends I have acquired in my own country and all over the world.

In Part One I wrote about my childhood and schooldays for our American grandchildren. This volume I have written for our many friends, Brita's and mine, throughout the world, whether scientists or laymen. I have made a special effort to write simply, so that even the chapters dealing with my scientific activities are not too technical for the ordinary reader to be able to share something of the excitement of being a scientist in the middle decades of the twentieth century.

G. Y. Z.

CHAPTER I

Conversation in a bathtub. — I start hunting pain nerve fibres. — A difficult dilemma.

"Now jump into the tub," said the sturdy woman in charge of the bath, and I did. She started to scrub my back, my front and finally my feet – thoroughly soaping them and keeping up a continuous conversation meanwhile. We had arrived in Stockholm the night before, having been suddenly called home as my mother was seriously ill and in hospital. We had rushed from the station to her sick-bed. We found her weak, but her physician, my elder brother Agne's close friend, Dr. Josua Tillgren, was optimistic. As our apartment had been let, we found a hotel close to the station. The bedroom had no connecting bathroom and you had to order a bath with a female bath attendant – a unique Swedish custom.

My brave lady of the bath was most entertaining. She told me that the year before the hotel was reserved for members attending the ecumenical church meeting presided over by our great Archbishop Nathan Söderblom. Priests from all Christian churches attended with the exception of the Roman Catholics. "One morning," said my bathing lady, "I prepared a bath for a priest with a long beard, a patriarch. When I entered, he gave a loud cry of alarm, but I pushed him down into the tub and said: Take it easy, old fellow, I won't kill you, and started to scrub his back. So he calmed down and finally he was purring like a cat and looking very pleased. In the afternoon, there was a procession of all these bearded priests to the porter's desk wanting to buy swimming trunks, and the next morning there was a long queue of priests who wanted me to bathe them."

1

My mother recovered slowly and after a few weeks was able to return to her home on Lidingö.

In 1927 I came back from 2 years' research work in Cambridge and London to the old physiology lab. in Stockholm, and started immediately to construct a gadget enabling me to record the impulse traffic of single sensory fibres, like Adrian's in Cambridge. Gustaf Jarl, my mechanic, helped me to make a copy of Keith Lucas's apparatus for drawing fine glass tubes to make a capillary electrometer. An old French microscope was adapted to it on an optic bench. Building a three-stage amplifier gave me the most trouble, however. The thermionic valves available at that time were very strongly microphonic. I therefore had to build a special box shielded by heavy lead plates to house the amplifier. As the lab. was shaken by the heavy street traffic around the corner at N. Mälarstrand, I found an underground room in the pathology building. I had to pass the mortuary to reach it and it was a very homely place, but it gave me two rooms and privacy.

When I was in Adrian's lab. in Cambridge I had become interested in the mechanism of pain. Pain has always had a peculiar status within the sensory system. Almost any stimulus, when it reaches sufficient strength, gives rise to pain. At that time (1927) many physiology or psychology textbooks were inclined to accept the old intensity theory that pain was elicited by all kinds of sensory nerve fibres when they were excited by a strong enough stimulation. I doubted this very much as I firmly believed that pain must be mediated by special nerve fibres.

I was very happy indeed when I finally got all the different parts of my electrical apparatus to function and I could demonstrate on a single nerve fibre preparation that the impulse transmission in sensory nerve fibres occurred according to frequency modulation, FM, a term which was not yet, however, in use in the telecommunication techniques of those days. Let me try to explain what it means by taking one example. A skin nerve is generally a bundle of a number of sensory fibres. By dividing that bundle and making cuts you can reduce the number of functioning fibres. If you are lucky, one single sensory fibre may remain active. Let us assume that this fibre has its end-organ, the receptor, in the skin. By pressing lightly on that part of the skin a small number of impulses (spikes) can be led off from the fibre. If you press harder the impulses occur more frequently. Each individual signal (spike) does not change with increasing strength of stimulation; only the frequency of discharge. This increases the safety of nervous transmission in the living body. If the impulses are dissipated locally during their transmission in the nerve fibres it does not reduce their effect on the central nervous system. It is the impulse frequency alone which signals the strength of the stimulus.

It is very simple: the nervous system is signalling with the simplest of all codes. It has only one sign – the spike – which follows the all-or-nothing principle, i.e. it is not changed, the nerve fibres always discharging the spike with the greatest strength which they can provide. Thus there is no amplitude modulation in the nerve fibres.

These fundamental principles of nervous transmission were first conceived by Adrian and me in Cambridge on a raw November day in 1925. So simple in a way, they have, however, often not been fully understood, even by neurophysiologists who ought to know better. The question of whether a sensory nerve fibre may mediate more than one sensory modality or quality has been open ever since the German, Johannes Müller, formulated his famous law of the specific sensory energies in 1825. It may be worth recounting how Müller, orginally more of a comparative anatomist, became interested in sensory physiology. In the 1820s a law case was much debated in German newspapers. A prominent citizen had been attacked and beaten one night by a political adversary and he subsequently sued him for damages. In the court the judge asked the plaintiff, "In the report you say that the night was so dark that you could not see your hand in front of your face. How could you tell then that it was the accused who attacked you?" "Your Honour," said the plaintiff, "It was very easy, in the flash of light which occurred when he hit me in the eye, I easily recognized the evil face of the accused." This created a fierce debate about whether the eyes of the cat radiated light and Johannes Müller was brought in to the discussion. He performed experiments which proved that, quite independent of the mode of stimulation of the sense organ (electrical, mechanical, etc.), the sensation experienced was always of the same kind – visual for the eye, acoustic for the ear, etc.

In 1882 Magnus Blix at Uppsala discovered that cold and warmth were only experienced when cooling or heating definite spots of the skin, the cold and warm spots. Thus he assumed that below these spots there existed in the skin special end-organs with "specific energies", which were selectively sensitive to cooling and warming respectively; receptors which signalled in specific nerve fibres running in separate and specific pathways to specific parts of the cerebral cortex. He conceived this as an extension of Müller's Law to include not only modalities but also qualities of sensation. Further, von Frey at Würzburg, in the 1890s, also maintained that pain was similarly directed from special spots only, although these were densely distributed in the skin – an opinion which was not, however, widely accepted.

Around the turn of the century two young men were working on their doctors' theses at Uppsala. They were Torsten Thunberg, who was a medical physiologist, and S. Alrutz, a young psychologist. Both of them studied pain elicited from the skin by various modes of stimulation and especially a phenomenon known as "the double pain sensation". If you prick a finger or a toe with a needle you immediately feel a pricking pain, followed after about a second by another pain which may have a somewhat different character and persists for a short while. Thunberg interpreted

4

this in the following way. The needle pricks the nerve fibres which leads to an immediate discharge – the first pain – while after a certain latency period the end-organ discharges into the nerve fibre, giving rise to the second, delayed, pain.

Alrutz, on the other hand, arrived at the assumption that the two pains were due to the stimulation of two different systems of pain mediating nerve fibres. It was mere conjecture on their part, as neither of them had any direct evidence to support their views. Thunberg, however, soon after became Professor of Physiology at Lund University following the premature death of Magnus Blix and was invited to contribute to the big German handbook edited by Nagel, where he strongly criticised Alrutz's thesis, maintaining his own theory. (My dear readers must excuse me for not disclosing until later who was right.)

As soon as I got my recording set in order, I started to lead off the electrical response from nerves running to the pads of the paws of the cat. When I touched the pad I got good responses to record, but to my great disappointment there was hardly any response at all from the nerve when I used radiating heat to burn the skin, in order to avoid any stimulation of the nerve end-organs responding to mechanical stimuli, touch or pressure. I repeated my experiments for months, increasing the amplification, but with no success. I realised that further amplification was of no use as it only increased the noise level. How could this be? A burning stimulation leads to strong avoiding reflexes and intense sensations of pain, and yet I saw hardly any response at all from the nerve. What a dilemma! It puzzled me for several years. Was it possible that pain was mediated by means other than volleys of impulses in nerve fibres or could it be that pain fibres conducted in the usual way but gave too small spikes to be detected by the present recording technique? I was more inclined to believe the latter alternative. When in 1929 I saw Gasser and Erlanger demonstrating to the International Congress of Physiology in Boston their disco-

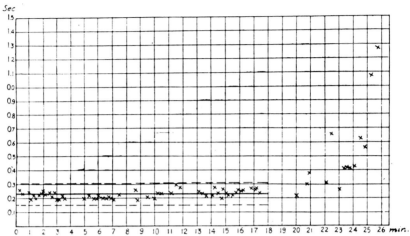

Chart showing the distribution of reaction times to a needle prick during compression of the upper arm. After 20 minutes the sensitivity to touch and pressure disappears.

Zotterman, Y., Peripheral nervous mechanism of pain,
Acta Med. Scand. (1933).

very of the very slow conduction of tiny non-myelinated nerve fibres in cutaneous nerves, I understood my failure, but I had no idea how to succeed. So I had to turn to psychophysical experiments. I started to record the reaction time of the first and second pain sensation. I found that the reaction time for the second pain, about 1 second, fitted in very well with the slow conduction rate of only 0.5 to 1.0 metres per second of the tiny non-myelinated fibres, named C-fibres by Gasser and Erlanger, while the first pain, for the same reason, could be attributed to medullated so-called A:delta fibres conducting at rates about 30 metres per second. Further, by inflating a cuff round the upper arm, as is done when the arterial blood pressure is measured, and arresting the blood flow, I found that touch and pressure were lost after about 18 minutes while pain could still be elicited; and that this pain showed a reaction time of about 1 second, corresponding to the "second pain".

On the evidence I was able to write my thesis in the spring of

6

1933 which I defended on 10 May 1933. It was only fifty pages, at that time, a very short dissertation on "The Peripheral Mechanism of Pain", accepted by Israel Holmgren, the editor of *Acta Medica Scandinavica* and my previous teacher in internal medicine. I will record the rather dramatic disputations in a special chapter. Let me add only that the disputation, although it gave me the lowest possible points for a further university career, nevertheless was a great turning point in my scientific work.

In the autumn of 1933 I became a *docent* (lecturer), but without a salary. I made my living doing three jobs: assistant in physiology with a salary of 175 Crowns per month, extra lecturer at G.C.I. for 300 Crowns a month and thirdly I had a post as medical officer in the Navy which gave me 200 Crowns a month, so we managed. Prices of food were comparatively low in the first part of the 1930s. A bottle of aquavit did not cost more than 1.50 Crowns and one could get a maidservant for only 30 Crowns a month. But serving those months every summer took most of the free time I should have devoted to my research work.

Nevertheless, I was pleased to receive research grants from the Andersson Fund at the Karolinska which enabled me to construct new apparatus for studying nervous conduction. Professor Hans Gertz had a brother, Ossian, at the Swedish Radio Company, a constructor of radio transmission stations. With his help I got a special amplifier built; it was a huge wooden case 4 feet by 1 foot 3 inches and 1 foot deep containing six valves, each compartment screened by heavy lead plate. It weighed some 130 pounds. This amplifier served me excellently, and was much more reliable than the previous ones which I had built myself. I now bought from Germany as a recording instrument a cathode-ray oscilloscope designed by von Ardenne, the great German electron engineer who later designed the electronics for the V_1 and V_2, Hitler's rockets in World War II, and who was taken prisoner by the Russians. His cathode-ray tubes gave excellent recordings. They were gas-filled and therefore only lasted a year or so, but I was exceedingly happy using them with a Leyboldt film camera. As a matter of fact, my recordings from early 1934 are technically as good as the best today (1970).

One day, when I was visiting Ossian Gertz in his electronics laboratory, I found an article by Johnson and Llewellyn in the *Bell Telephone Technical Bulletin*. Its title was "Signal-to-noise Ratio in Thermionic Valves". I shall never forget how thrilled I was on realising that this paper resolved the dilemma I had met when trying to record the impulses in the tiny pain fibres. I understood that I had to make very thin nerve preparations in order to obtain a signal-to-noise ratio for the tiniest sensory fibres to enable me to record their spikes. Hitherto these had been entirely masked by the noise level originating from the thermal agitation of the input circuit. Part of this was due to internal noise of the first valve. Ossian Gertz kindly met my request to select from a hundred valves those with the lowest possible internal noise. In that way I got valves with only a third as much noise as other commercial valves.

But this was not enough. I had to increase the signals, the spikes. This could only be done by decreasing the diameter of the nerve preparation between the off leads. A sensory nerve bundle contains a great number of nerve fibres of different diameters, each fibre discharging spikes of the same voltage. When you lead off from such a bundle, the large fibres yield large spikes in comparison to the small fibres. If you could lead off from single fibres, they would all give spikes of the same voltage, but when you are leading off from a bundle, a small fibre gives only a very small fraction of its voltage, because all the non-active fibres are short-circuiting. Let me explain it this way; in a nerve bundle of 1 millimetre diameter, with a fibre of 0.01 millimetre diameter, you cannot lead off more than at most one-hundredth of the intrinsic voltage, i.e. 400 microvolts. As the nerve preparation has a moist surface

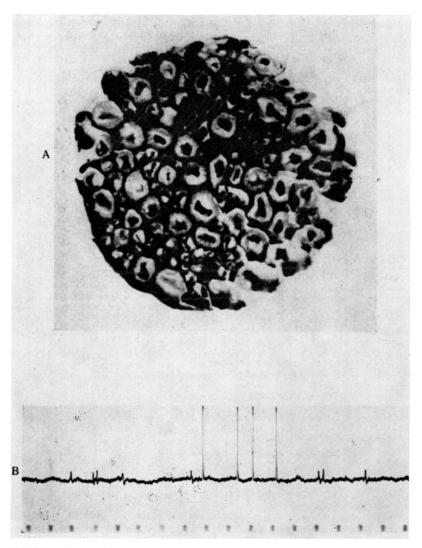

(A) Microphoto of lingual nerve preparation. Magnification 940. Largest fibres measure 10 μ in diameter. Alsheimer-Mann stain. (B) Records from the same preparation showing the ratio between the amplitudes of cold and touch potentials. The irregular discharge of cold impulses is due to the exposure of the tongue to air. The four large spikes were elicited by touching the tongue with a brush. Zotterman, Y., Specific action potentials in the lingual nerve of cat. Skand. Arch. f. Physiol. 75, 105 (1936).

as well, you generally get only a third of this, let us say about 100 microvolts. Such a preparation has an ohmian resistance which gives rise to a noise level of 10 microvolts, thus the signal-to-noise ratio will be 100/10 = 10:1, and you want to record from a fibre of only 0.0005 millimetre in diameter. Then because of the short-circuit you cannot expect more than 5 microvolts which will be hidden in a noise level of 10 microvolts. But there was an escape from this dilemma. By further reduction of the diameter of the nerve bundle, I could increase the signals of small fibres by reducing the short-circuit of inactive tissue. This of course increased the noise as it increased the resistance between the off leads, but only with the square root of the diameter, while the signals from the single fibres increased linearly with the diameter of the nerve preparation between the electrodes.

When I got my new electronic set-up in 1934 I was very anxious to test whether my calculations would prove correct. Leading off from fine strands of the lingual nerve, which supplies the anterior three-fifths of the tongue with sensory fibres, I stimulated the surface of the tongue with different adequate (natural) stimuli. My calculations proved right. Light mechanical stimulation (a touch of a strand of wool) gave rise to large spikes, while cooling elicited spikes from smaller myelinated fibres. Heating the surface of the tongue with water as hot as would give a burning sensation on one's own tongue caused the appearance of quite low and distinct spikes obviously deriving from very small and slowly conducting fibres. These tiny spikes would also occur when a mechanical stimulus was increased to a painful strength. I realised that I had reached my goal. I had been able to record the impulse traffic in the tiniest of all sensory fibres, the class C-fibres, according to Gasser and Erlanger's nomenclature for nerve fibres, and I was very happy when in the spring of 1935 I could hand in a manuscript to Professor Göran Liljestrand, the editor of *Skandinavisches Archiv für Physiologie* which was printed in Leip-

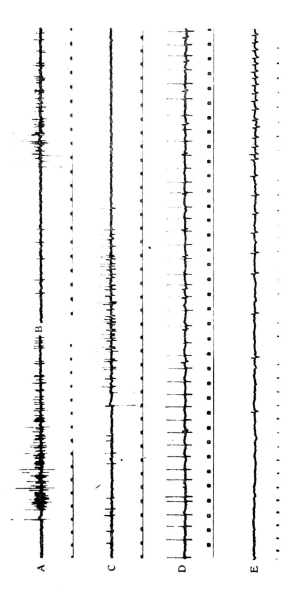

Afferent spike potentials from different sensory fibres of a fine strand of the lingual nerve of the cat when applying different stimuli to the tongue. (A) The effect of a drop of water of 14°C. falling on the tongue. (B) First the effect of a faint puff of air which does not cause any visible deformation of the surface, followed by the effect of a stronger puff of air which ma' es a definite deformation. (C) A drop of 80°C. falling upon the tongue. (D) The effect of pressing a pointed rod into the tongue. (E) Squirting hot water (60°C.) over the tongue. Zotterman, Y., Specific action potentials in the lingual nerve of cat. Skand. Arch. f. Physiol. 75, 105 (1936).

zig. I was convinced that I had proved that the largest cutaneous nerve fibres did not mediate pain, that cold and warmth were conducted in separate specific fibres and, finally, that noxious (painful) stimuli excited endings of tiny nonmedullated nerve fibres of the C-class as I had suggested from more indirect evidence in my dissertation in 1933. When in the following spring (1936) my paper was printed and circulated, I received a very kind letter of congratulation from Bryan Matthews at Cambridge, who had constructed a very handy iron tongue oscillograph for the recording of the nerve responses. He was to succeed Adrian as head of the famous Cambridge Physiology Laboratory.

But apart from this my paper was not much commented on or perhaps it was only really understood by a few specialists. The *Skandinavisches Archiv* did not have a wide international circulation. One of my records, however (that on page nine here), was reproduced in John Fulton's *Textbook of Physiology* in the 1940s. Nevertheless, I had to go on collecting more direct experimental evidence for my ideas. I had read how old William Harvey, throughout the whole of his long life, never lost any opportunity to collect new proofs for his discovery of the circulation of the blood.

CHAPTER II

The Minnekahda *voyage, 1929. — The International Physiology Congress in Boston, Woods Hole and New York, 1929. — The homecoming. — Brita has food poisoning.*

At the closing session of the Twelfth International Physiological Congress in Stockholm, 1926, in the Hall of Uppsala University, Joseph Erlanger, Secretary of the American Physiological Society, moved that the next congress should be held in 1929 in the United States of America. The motion was carried unanimously. During the discussion A. J. Carlson of Chicago remarked: "There are many millionaires in the United States, but they are not members of our Physiological Society." Great generosity was shown, however, and a large number of travelling grants from the U.S.A. enabled young European physiologists to attend the Boston Congress.

It was the rule that the president of the former congress should act as Chairman of the permanent International Physiological Committee until the National Congress Committee elected the president of the next congress. In May 1927 Professor J. E. Johansson of Stockholm received a letter from Professor Howell at Baltimore informing him that the Federation of American Societies for Experimental Biology had, at their spring meeting, appointed a National Committee to take care of all matters pertaining to the congress. The committee consisted of Professors Erlanger, Lusk, MacLeod, and Howell for the Physiological Society, Professors Mendel, Shaffer, and van Slyke for the Biochemical Society, Professors Abel and Sollmann for the Pharmacological Society, and Professors Warthin and W. H. Brown for the Society of Experimental Pathology.

At its first meeting the committee decided on Boston as the venue for the congress, and Professor Cannon of Harvard University was asked to act as Chairman of the Local Committee to make the necessary arrangements.

In October 1927 H. E. Roaf, Secretary of the Physiological Society of Great Britain, wrote to Johansson that, at a meeting on October 15th 1927, the society had discussed the forthcoming congress in Boston. "It was suggested," wrote Roaf, "that Professor A. V. Hill should act for the British physiologists in making arrangements for the congress. The late Professor Starling was our representative on the International Committee, and we believe that no successor to him can be officially appointed until the congress meets." Subsequently Johansson wrote Howell a letter proposing that "the International Committee appointed by the 1926 Congress call in A. V. Hill if questions referring to the participation of British physiologists in the next congress should be submitted to the committee's decision. Such a case may possibly occur but it is very unlikely, as the responsibility for the next congress has been taken by such competent persons as the American National Committee and the functionaries whom it has elected."

Already, at the end of the 1926 Congress, Ernest Starling had suggested that a ship should be chartered to take the European physiologists across the Atlantic. During the first half of 1928 A. V. Hill examined different approaches to this idea, and at the May meeting of the Physiological Society he put forward a proposal to travel to Boston by a single-class ship. This meeting had been arranged in conjunction with the Harvey Tercentenary, and the many continental physiologists present gave their consent.

In June 1928 the German Physiological Society sent out a circular signed by Höber, Bethe, Embden, and Thomas inviting their members to participate in Hill's voyage. And although they had found that the German lines Hapag and Lloyd could offer transportation from Cuxhaven at a still lower price, they felt the advantages of a one-class boat for all European physiologists to be so great that national considerations should be set aside.

14

Captain Jensen

The S. S. *Minnekahda* was a triple-screw steamer of 17,281 tons, built during World War I for the transport of soldiers between the United States and Europe. It was a single-class ship that gave every passenger access to all the decks and to all social events on board. It belonged to the Atlantic Transport Line sailing under the U. S. flag. For this trip it was booked for about 400 physiologists and their families, who embarked at Tilbury in the Thames estuary on Friday, 9 August 1929. Later in the day she called at Boulogne, taking on board another 370 passengers for Boston and New York. Among these there were about 200 secretaries returning from a

A group with A. V. Hill in the centre. From the left, back row: Gaddum, Leyko, Poulton, Liljestrand. Flanking Hill: Clark and Verney with de Burgh Daly in profile. Below: G. Stella and J. Bouckaert.

European trip. They were young American girls whose presence added a certain colour to the life on deck, particularly to the dancing at night.

The first hours on board were the scene of happy reunions of colleagues who had not met for some years. At the previous congresses, in Edinburgh in 1923 and especially in Stockholm in 1926, communications between physiologists had been reopened, the gulf between the former combatants of World War I was bridged and it was a very happy gathering that met on the *Minnekahda*. As I had worked in the 1926 Congress Bureau, I recognized most of the delegates. Among the older scientists I remember Abderhalden, von Brücke from Innsbruck, Botazzi from Naples, Joseph Barcroft from Cambridge, A. Bethe from Frankfurt on Main, Orbeli

16

Lady physiologists from Bedford College. Standing: The Misses Henderson, M. Pickford and M. Bond. Sitting: Mary Brazier, Mrs. Ogden, Miss Chen, Miss Stevens and Professor Murray. In the life belt, Miss Stratford.

from Moscow, Tschermak-Zeisenegg from Prague, Foa from Turin, L. Asher with his wife from Bern, Verzar with his wife from Szeged, Otto Loewi from Graz, H. J. Jordan from Holland, Walter Fletcher from London, and Henry Dale. The two latter were both very actively engaged in all kinds of sports events on the decks. And so, of course, were A. V. Hill and Albert Szent-Gyorgyi, with his beautiful wife Nellie, and Dr. Mary Pickford, the undisputed belle of the British women physiologists, Göran Liljestrand, General Secretary of the 1926 Congress, Basil Verney, Jack Gaddum, I. de Burgh Daly, F. Bremer from Brussels, Rodolfo Margaria from Milan, Carl Tigerstedt from Helsingfors, Parnas from Warsaw, the Ebbeckes from Bonn, U. S. Von Euler from Stockholm, and of course the previous Congress President, J. E. Johansson. Among the new French delegates I remember Mayer, and I remember, too, a large group of Spanish delegates gathered around Pi Suñer.

17

A Swedish-speaking group. From the left standing: J. Olow, Stockholm; G. Wendt, Helsingfors; G. Liljestrand, Stockholm; J. E. Johansson, Stockholm; E. Agduhr, Uppsala; Sitting: U. S. von Euler, Stockholm; C. Tigerstedt, Helsing-fors; Y. Zotterman, Stockholm; H. Rydin, Uppsala and G. Ahlgren, Lund.

Life on Board

How life on board was spent is cogently expressed in an after-dinner speech Professor Johansson gave at the Captain's dinner the night before we arrived in the port of Boston.

The experiences from these past days appear to many of us like a voyage in Wonderland. The more ingenious of us have even expressed our astonishment in scientifically formulated questions. The remarkable thing is that all these questions have been answered in the same way. I will just give a few examples. Immediately after the embarkation one heard many of the most prominent scientists asking the question: How can six robust fellows sleep in a cabin with only four beds? Then with devotional silence we followed the contours of the coast famous from so many songs. So

18

an agitated voice was heard: How can we arrive at a congress in America while still having the English coast in sight? Both questions were answered. The Captain arranges it.

After a few days' voyage another question arose: How can such highly cultivated people live without lectures? Even that problem was solved by our amiable Captain, who always demonstrated his ability to discover within our circle the most prominent talents in different spheres.

Shuffleboard and deck tennis became our favourite sports, in which the members of the English group, with their greater experience of long sea voyages, were particularly successful. Henry Dale's prowess at deck tennis was only terminated by an attack of lumbago at the end of the cruise. Walter Flechter, who often played with Dr. Mary Pickford, was also very good at the game. They were a very beautiful couple to watch. The same applies to Albert

Otto Loewi demonstrating a new hat mode to K. Felix and A. V. Hill.   August Krogh.

E. von Brücke and Henry Dale.

and Nellie Szent-Györgyi. Howard Florey, Basil Verney, Göran Liljestrand, and Gaddum often played with me.

At the shuffleboard you saw the steadier boys like Parnas, and Agduhr from Uppsala, both in the heavyweight class. In spite of his enormous bulk, Parnas was quite agile, particularly at night, when he danced nearly every dance. And he was a beautiful dancer; he did the tango particularly well. I once asked my wife how she liked dancing with him. "Wonderful," she said, "I felt as if I were dancing with an enormous eiderdown quilt."

Somebody suggested that we should arrange a tug-of-war competition between the various nations. The British were able to set up several teams. We tried to collect a Swedish team with Agduhr as anchor, but he refused, for anatomical reasons. Then A. V. Hill, who was considered rather too slim by the British, joined us and was declared an "honorary Swede". The Poles had Parnas as their anchor. They were, however, easily beaten by the Italian team, who were very keen to win the tournament in order to be able to send a victorious wireless message to Mussolini, or so

P. Eggleton and D. Bronk playing deck tennis.

somebody insinuated. Watching the Italians pull the Polish team along the deck with Parnas as anchor I heard Sonovsky, pointing at Parnas, comment to A. V. Hill: "That fellow must be filled with air."

A. V. Hill told me that while working in England Parnas admired his flannels, so he took him to his tailor. "What about the price?" asked Parnas. "It depends on how much cloth it will take," replied the tailor, taking his enormous measurements. To Parnas's great regret the making up of the flannels was somewhat delayed. "It took Our Lord only six days to create the whole world and you have taken six weeks to make my flannels," complained Parnas. "Yes, but look at the world," replied the tailor.

Meals and Other Diversions

As usual on board ship we were served many and pretty substantial meals. We became acquainted with the huge American breakfast of fruit, cereals, bacon and eggs, flapjacks with maple syrup, coffee, and tea. Between meals we were supplied with beautiful oranges, as many as we liked, cold and tasty from the refrigerated stores. In the dining saloon we were seated at round tables for eight persons. I sat beside Marie Krogh, a charming and witty lady with an M.D. degree who took a very active part in her husband's respiratory experiments. Her Danish as well as her English was much easier to follow than was that of the famous August Krogh. They were accompanied by their lovely young blonde daughter Ellen. The food was plentiful and good. No wine or liquor was served on board, as prohibition was still in force in the U. S., and even the officers were strictly forbidden to bring any liquor on board for private consumption. I cannot remember that there were any complaints about this. There was certainly no need for any "artificial stimulation", as our friend Liljestrand, a militant temperance man, used to call it.

The weather was excellent, and we had nice warm days until we reached the Greenland Current, which cooled the atmosphere very markedly. Starkenstein, the famous pharmacologist of Prague, had the brilliant idea of testing his new drug against seasickness (Vasano) on the 400 physiologists – a unique opportunity. But there was only a slight swell and we could see him become more and more melancholy, climbing to the bridge and looking out over an almost unrippled ocean.

We met a few ships, and one day a huge whale displayed his remarkable ability to act as a fountain, squirting water to a height of at least 60 feet. We also enjoyed the presence of a few wind-

22

driven migrating birds who found rest on the ship. As they refused to eat bread or meat, some of us spent hours searching for insects to feed them.

Life on board was indeed very pleasant. We non-British passengers used these days to brush up our English, and I took the opportunity of learning a good deal of American slang and expressions not taught in the schools. At night we danced on deck, the young officers of the ship having a great choice among the 200 American girls. One night a fancy-dress ball was arranged and I lent my evening dress with stiff shirt and white tie and my *chapeau claque* to a young lady who carried it off beautifully, many years before Ginger Rogers made her big hit on the screen in the picture *Top Hat* with Fred Astaire. (It may have been Ginger Rogers, after all; I have forgotten her name.) Other nights we were entertained by Professor Jordan playing the flute. In the Spanish group there was a tiny dark-eyed lady, the daughter of the famous composer Granados, who played her father's compositions on the piano. I envied her fine technique. She was particularly clever with her left hand, which is a very necessary accomplishment when playing Granados's piano music, with its intricate and characteristically Spanish rhythms.

Scientific Activities

Most of the physiologists, of course, had to "talk shop". On the very second day lectures and conferences were arranged. Orbeli was anxious to discuss his experiments on the effect of sympathetic stimulation on fatigued muscles. Barcroft told us about the long periods he had spent in low-pressure chambers. A. V. Hill discussed with the Eggletons their finding of "phosphagen" in muscles and its relation to heat production. Einar Lundsgaard in Copenhagen had just made his discovery that a muscle could contract without setting free any lactic acid and had gone to Meyerhof in Berlin. "The revolution in muscle physiology" had been *in*

From left, above: C. Tigerstedt, Helsinki; U. S. von Euler, Stockholm; H. Rydin, Stockholm; below: J. Olow, Stockholm (obstetrician); E. Agduhr, Stockholm; A. V. Hill, London; G. Liljestrand, Stockholm.

statu nascenti ever since Embden's report, in 1926, that lactic acid was only liberated after the contraction.

Many of the younger British physiologists took the opportunity of discussing with Walter Fletcher their future research plans. Fletcher was the secretary of the British Medical Research Council and a wonderful adviser. His great erudition and experience and his readiness to help were highly appreciated.

Among the Germans, U. Ebbecke from Bonn and Herman Rein from Göttingen were both extremely versatile scientists, whose experience extended over vast territories. Mrs. Ebbecke was a talented painter of quite high professional skill. There was also *der sehr gemütliche* Professor Wilhelm Steinhausen from Greisswald, demonstrating his beautiful experiments on the deviation of the uvula in the ampulla of the pike's semicircular canal. I believe it was he who told me the following anecdote. The great Helmholtz was once asked by a lady at the dinner table: "Tell me, Your

24

Excellency, what is the difference between concave and concrete?"
"It is just the same as the difference between Gustave and Guest-
house," replied Helmholtz.[1]

Corneille Heymans had every reason to be happy, as he had just
discovered the chemoceptive influence from the carotid body on
respiration. He was, however, somewhat worried about the respiratory physiologists of the old school, who were not prepared to
accept his views. It was to take another ten years of wonderful
experiments by Heymans and his school in Ghent, and the direct
recording of the afferent inflow from the carotid body by another
passenger on board, the Venetian Giulio Stella, and by me, to
convince them. But then Heymans was awarded the Nobel Prize
(1939). He was always very entertaining, and had an enormous
store of anecdotes, of which I remember only the following. Mrs.
Webster one morning found Mr. Webster *(of Webster's Dictio-
nary)* kissing her chambermaid, so she exclaimed: "Mr. Webster,
I am surprised!" "Mrs. Webster," said Mr. Webster calmly, "how
many times have I to remind you about the proper use of these
difficult words? *We* were surprised, *you* were astonished, my dear."

The Spanish group was quite numerous, headed by Pi Suñer from
Barcelona and around him Carasco di Formiguera and young Severo
Ochoa, who had just started working in Meyerhof's laboratory.
Thirty years later Ochoa received a Nobel Prize. Another of Meyer-
hof's young associates on board was Lohmann, who made funda-
mental contributions to muscle enzyme chemistry.

Otto Loewi from Graz was one of the liveliest talkers, always
ready for a new joke. He was headed for a Nobel Prize, which
he was to share with another shipmate, Henry Dale (1935).
Altogether we had on board no fewer than nine physiologists who
have since received the Nobel Prize in "Physiology or Medicine",
as it is officially styled. The reason for this is that the great donor

---

[1] "Excellenz, was ist der Unterschied zwischen konkav und konkret?" "Ach,
das ist gerade derselber als der Unterschied zwischen Gustav und Gasthof."

Alfred Nobel was particularly interested in physiological problems. He even started some research on blood transfusion in Paris in 1890 with J. E. Johansson.

Among the European scientists there were also a few well-known Americans, such as H. M. Evans, who in spite of being a professor of anatomy at Berkeley made his famous contributions to the physiology of the pituitary. A. V. Hill, finding that medical students spent too much time on anatomy, used to say: "What is the use of anatomy? It has never been of any use to me." I remember that he got somewhat red in the face, though he did not kick me out, when I replied: "I think we have noticed that."

Detlev Bronk, who had spent a year in England working with A. V. Hill and with Adrian, helped me to put my translations of Johansson's afterdinner speeches into correct English. He also told me about his work with Adrian on single motor nerve fibres and about advances in the electronic technique, which I found very interesting and helpful.

We lived in a very happy historical era. World War I had not been forgotten, of course, but the previous congresses in 1923 and in 1926 had broken the isolation of political blocs: the Russian and East European colleagues fraternised freely. The world-wide economic depression had not yet started, and Hitler was an unknown ex-soldier. It was a happy world, which believed in evolution and in the League of Nations. There were quite a few young men among us whose dreams of new discoveries were to come true after a few years.

Albert Szent-Györgyi planned to go to the livestock market in Chicago after the congress to collect enough adrenals for his research. It resulted in his isolation of a crystallised substance that a few years later he found to be vitamin C. He received the Nobel Prize in 1937 for "his discoveries in connection with the biological combustion processes, with special reference to vitamin C and the catalysis of fumaric acid". Two very popular young men on board were G. L. Brown, the present Sir Lindor, who was the President of I.U.P.S. 1956–1968, and Howard Florey, later Lord Florey, Australian born, who was about that time starting on pathological physiology. He was also to be awarded the Nobel Prize for his contribution to the discovery and production of penicillin. U.S. von Euler was among the very youngest of us all. In Thunberg's laboratory in Lund he had just started his first experiments on adrenaline, using Thunberg's methylene blue method. His work on the sympathetic transmitter substance was to culminate in his famous book *Nor-adrenalin* in 1956, and a few years later he was appointed President of the Board of the Nobel Foundation.[1]

Basil Verney, who had been working in Starling's laboratory on the regulation of the urinary flow, was close to his discovery of the diencephalic control of the release of the antidiuretic hormone. Bronk was planning his important research on the transmission in sympathetic ganglia. It was an exciting time. We perhaps now live in a still more exciting period, but in 1929 we were not so many as we are today. The physiological journals proper hardly exceeded a dozen, and the number of papers one had to read was certainly less than 10% of the present output. We had thus time to listen and reflect and to discuss all the various physiological fields, and we felt united in our glorious class of "life scientists".

Conclusion

The last night on board we were served, as was the rule, a special meal, the Captain's Dinner, and Johansson extended our thanks to the jovial Captain Jensen in the after-dinner speech quoted above. On this occasion Johansson also addressed A. V. Hill in another speech, the notes of which I found in Johansson's archive.

---

[1] He received the Nobel Prize in 1970.

Ladies and Gentlemen.

The idea of a common journey such as this was suggested at the closing of the last congress by our late colleague Starling. The one whom we must thank for the realisation of that idea is, as you all know, A. V. Hill. Everyone who has the experience of what it means to unite such a number of people in a common enterprise will appreciate what our colleague Hill has done for us. It is easy to perceive the general contentment of everybody. Your kind look, Professor Hill, gives us the clue to your success. We extend to you our heartiest thanks.

Then A. V. Hill rose and suggested that we should send a wireless message to Professor Cannon, Chairman of the Congress Bureau at Harvard, telling him of the twenty nationalities we had on board. It ended "Cubanos, Chinks and Yanks".

The following morning outside Boston's harbor a tug appeared, from which Meakins and Redfield climbed on board the *Minne-kahda* to welcome us to Boston. They told us that we would be relieved of the usual tedious disembarking procedures, a much appreciated concession in view of the prevailing temperature of 35°C in the dock barracks. Within an hour we were all transported by bus to the various dormitories of Harvard University.

A couple of episodes from our disembarkment are worth mentioning. In the crowded customs barracks I recognised the Swedish-born Otto Folin, Professor of Biochemistry at Harvard anxiously looking for his friend Johansson, who was invited to stay with the Folins. So I went up to him and said: "Professor Folin, if you are looking for Professor Johansson, he is standing at the desk marked J-K." "Have we met before?" asked Folin. "No, Sir," I said. "Oh," said Folin with a wry smile, "you recognised me of course because I am the ugliest fellow in the world." The famous Folin was a tall slender man, his face unfortunately disfigured by an operation.

There were also Professor and Mrs. Cannon to welcome us. Mrs. Cannon had just published a long novel, *Red Rust,* about a Swedish-born farmer in Minnesota. She was a very charming and vivacious lady. Johansson used to tell about their first meeting in Langley's house at the 1898 Congress in Cambridge. Mrs Langley, a beautiful lady of Scottish descent, was showing them glass pictures in their windows, representing portraits and castles in Scotland belonging to her ancestors. "This was my great grandfather, who was the Lord Provost," etc. After listening to this for a while Mrs. Cannon suddenly exclaimed: "How different from us. My maternal grandfather stole horses in Kentucky and was hanged."

It was unbearably hot in the customs sheds in Boston, but in half an hour we were put in buses which brought us to the Vanderbilt Hall Dormitories at Harvard. Carrying a heavy bag up five storeys made me even hotter. I had never before experienced such a high temperature. It was 92°F, and the humidity was very high. I took a cold shower but found no relief. I took my temperature and found it was 39.2°. I was rather alarmed, so I laid down naked on the bed, took a sleeping pill and fell asleep at 7 p.m. I was woken up by a frightful thunderstorm 6 hours later and felt very well after the atmosphere had cleared.

In the morning I registered at the Congress Bureau in the marvellous marble building of Harvard Medical School. There were 1600 members from thirty-seven different nations -- 1000 more than the previous Congress in Stockholm in 1926. At the opening, August Krogh from Copenhagen gave an excellent lecture on the Progress of Physiology, when he suggested that the Physiological Congresses should serve other purposes than to arrange congresses. He said: "The International Congress of Physiology is without doubt the highest authority in matters pertaining to the organization of physiology and its necessary services. Why should not the Congress extend this authority? We meet together for friendly intercourse, to be taught and to teach by demonstration of experiments and discussion of papers. The benefit to our science from a meeting like this is very great, although difficult to measure by tangible results. Why should we not also make this Congress, which meets together, into an instrument for the organization of essential services for the elaboration of rules of nomenclature and for the protection of our scientific freedom? I believe that it can be done and ought to be done."

Krogh was a prophet. The Physiology Congresses today perform many such functions, since the physiologists founded the I.U.P.S. (International Union of Physiological Sciences) which is part of I.C.S.U., the International Council of Scientific Unions under Unesco. The last Congress in 1968 in Washington D.C. attracted more than 4000 members, among them about 600 from Europe.

Few scientific institutions in the world can offer such advantages for a physiology congress as the Harvard Medical School. Round the campus with the magnificent administration building in the background at Longwood Avenue, four huge laboratory buildings were situated, each containing well-equipped laboratories and modern lecture halls. The middle building offered excellent premises for the Congress Bureau, Post Office, Telegraph Branch and Travelling Bureau. The campus and the terrace in the front was a general meeting place during the Congress itself, where you revived old acquaintances and made new ones – and were photographed. One evening the Boston Symphonic Orchestra gave a wonderful concert there, the buildings illuminated by a full moon. There I heard for the first time the Rhapsody in Blue by Gershwin, beautifully executed. It was a night I shall never forget.

As prohibition reigned in the United States no wines or liquor were served at the banquet, but all our American friends carried hip flasks of liquor which were generously poured into coffee cups.

I was rather lazy in attending the transactions and listened only to papers within my field of research and they were not many – but I remember the papers given by Detlev Bronk, Herbert Gasser,

30

Edwin Cohen and R. Redfield outside Harvard Medical School, 1929.

Dr. Warbasse's residence at Penzance Point, Woods Hole, Massachusetts, 1929.

Joseph Erlanger, Harry Grundfest and a few others. Most of the time I spent talking and discussing problems with my American colleagues. At the closing session Brita's uncle, Professor Johansson, gave a speech which I have preserved.

My friend Selig Hecht introduced me to a young girl, Miss Agnes Warbasse, whose father, a retired surgeon, had a big house on Penzance Point at Woods Hole, near the main Biological Station, to which we were invited after the Congress. She took me and two elderly Professors – von Fürth from Vienna and another from Milan – out there in her little motor car on the last evening. I was rather embarrassed when she put me beside her in the front seat of her small convertible and the two older men in the small "dicky" seat at the back. But she insisted it was because they spoke very poor English.

Her father had indeed a wonderful house. We had a delicious supper and I slept in a room which I shared with Professor von

Fürth, a most lovable old fellow in his early sixties. About noon the following day the other European physiologists arrived by train and Brita's uncle was driven out to Warbasse's house.

Dr. Warbasse was a fine, magnificently built man, just 60. He had had a very fine practice as a surgeon in New York. His chief interest was, however, co-operation, and he became a great figure in International Co-operation. He came originally from a Danish family who emigrated to the United States. They were free thinkers. Dr. Warbasse interested me greatly as he believed that religion had caused much hatred and war, so the Warbasses had been brought up for three generations without any religious teaching. They were a lovely family.

Dr. Warbasse took us down to a small jetty on the north side of the Point. There we put on swimming trunks and dived from the high springboard, very gracefully. So did Uncle Jöns, to my great satisfaction. But our Austrian and Italian friends ran behind the bushes, they were not used to such activities. There were very strong currents. We swam out for about 100 yards, then a strong current took us with great speed to the edge of the peninsula. Then we followed Dr. Warbasse, swimming about 100 yards southwards, where we reached a strong current which rapidly took us about half a mile to the south side of the narrow peninsula where we landed and walked back about 150 yards to the starting-point of our swimming tour. It was indeed very pleasant.

In the evening, Dr. Warbasse invited all of us to a great clam bake on the shore. There we had clams, oysters and lobsters, all beautifully cooked, our American friends supplying us with a variety of drinks from their hip flasks; it was a wonderful moonlit night.

I was most grateful to Celia and Selig Hecht, who had arranged our stay with the Warbasses. Dr. Warbasse lived there until 1965, when, at the age of over 90, he sold the place, which was one of the most beautiful spots in New England.

The following evening we were taken over to New Bedford, where we embarked on a big paddle steamer, *Providence,* which took us down to New York during the night. This was a new experience for me. The cabins were quite spacious! They contained one broad and comfortable bed and a narrow one over it. I asked "Sparky", the radio operator – a Swede – about this. "Oh, don't you know? This is a ship for honeymooners!"

"But do so many newly-wed couples go on honeymoons?" "Don't be naïve," he said. "A wedding ring costs no more than a dime in Woolworths."

We spent a wonderful evening together on the boat. I remember that I had a long talk with Charles Lovatt Evans, who was full of anecdotes. Unhappily I have forgotten all but a few of them and these, unfortunately, are not respectable enough for a book!

The next morning we steamed down the East River and I saw the New York skyscrapers for the first time. Our New York colleagues had arranged a fine programme for us. We visited the new Medical Centres of Cornell University; we were taken out to the Long Island estate of the famous jeweller Tiffany, who had an art school there; Professor Graham Lusk, the great physiologist, was married to his daughter. My old classmate, Birger Nordholm, head of the Swedish State Railways Information Office in 5th Avenue, took me out to Coney Island, giving me drinks in coffee cups at various "speakeasys".

At Coney Island Birger Nordholm insisted that we should go on the biggest switchback, "The Cyclone". He put me in the last seat of the set of cars and put himself and his secretary in one of the first cars. We were very carefully fastened to the seats by both arms and legs. What an enormous downwards swoop and a soaring up again! I wonder how many G's. While we were rushing through the air I saw something glittering in the searchlight.

It was my silver watch that I carried loose in my breast pocket. It was the last I saw of that old friend, which I had been given at my matriculation in 1916. When I was finally let out of the car, I could hardly stand on my feet. When later that evening over a cup of raw whisky in the restaurant Florence in New York City, I told the Swedish Consul General about it, he said, "For Heaven's sake, The Cyclone! It is only circus artists who go on that." I had large blue bruises on my thighs and upper arms for quite some weeks after and Brita jokingly refused to believe my story of how I came by them, or how I lost my watch.

The first night I took Dr. Sybil Cooper down town with me from our rooms in Columbia University dormitories; I remember how we stopped in Central Park, to look at the wonderful skyline. I was really jumping with joy, but she stood there silent, not saying a word. "For Heaven's sake say something! Don't you feel anything, seeing this for the first time?" I said, taking her by the shoulders and shaking her a little. "Oh", she said, "You know we English are brought up like this – not to show our emotions."

It was such hot August weather that I had to buy a straw hat, which I got for a dollar at the south end of Manhattan, where I went to see the very fine statue of John Ericsson, the great Swedish inventor. But I lost it soon after, as I left it on a bench at Columbia for a few minutes. A horse came up and ate it!

On our way back from the Boston Congress we boarded the S.S. *Olympia* in New York. It was a very large liner of 55,000 tons with passengers in three classes. Brita's uncle and most of the physiologists on this ship travelled in the Tourist 3 class at the extreme back of the ship, which vibrated all the time from the three propellers. We had a pleasant crossing in a rather calm North Atlantic. I remember that Uncle Jöns quite enjoyed himself. Although a bachelor in his sixty-eighth year and rather harshly treated by his eldest sister, who ruled both him and his household, he was by no means insensitive to ladies of charm. He was a very talented raconteur. I saw him for days on end engaged in lively conversation with an English lady, promenading on the deck and offering her tea and coffee. So much so, as a matter of fact, that her husband finally began to look somewhat jealous.

When, after seven days, we disembarked at Southampton, I received a letter from Brita, whom I had left with friends in North Wales. She told me that she had been ill but was getting better and that she would meet us at Victoria Station in London. I felt rather alarmed, of course, and when the train drew into the station I looked anxiously for her on the platform, but I could not see her. Searching amongst the crowd I found her behind a pillar, looking somewhat thin and pale. "What is the matter?" I said, after embracing her. "Oh", she said, "I have been rather sick. They took me into a nursing home at Rhos Bay in Wales. The doctor thought I had food poisoning because I vomited so much and couldn't eat, but I think I am going to have a baby." Oh, how happy I was! We had been married for 6 years and were longing for a child. Brita must be right; it was not food poisoning that she was suffering from, it was hyperemesis gravidarum, to give it its medical term. I had been taught how to treat this disorder by one of my teachers in obstetrics, Professor Forssner. When I kissed her I could smell acetone on her breath, a sure sign that she was starving. In the nursing home she had been offered rice, soups, boiled fish, etc., all with no flavour. After a week the doctor asked her what she would like to eat and drink. He only shook his head when she said: "Irish stew and stout."

So as soon as we had arrived at our hotel in Bloomsbury Uncle Jöns, Brita and I took a taxi to our favourite restaurant in Soho, the Gennaros in Upper Compton Road, and there I ordered a lobster stew and a large bottle of Orvieto, Italian white wine. And to her great surprise, Brita kept it down. It was the first meal she had been able to keep in her stomach for more than a fortnight. I was anxious to give her tasty food and she generally retained it but, of course, crossing the North Sea on a smaller Swedish Lloyd boat was hard for her. When we reached home in Stockholm and our apartment in Jungfrugatan I rushed round to my mother and other relatives to tell them that Brita was going to have a baby. I even rushed into the hospital ward of our young friend Hugo Theorell, who two days earlier had been operated on for appendicitis, shouting "Would you believe it, Brita is going to have a baby." In the state he was in, he did not much care, as he was often given to telling us afterwards in his histrionic manner!

Poor Brita had a very difficult first three months of pregnancy. In those days I was a smoker, and the smell of tobacco made her sick. I managed, however, to keep her properly fed and her sickness disappeared; after three months she carried on in magnificent health, working in the lab. until the very last weeks. Furthermore, she even took a class in cooking three nights a week, from 6 to 9 p.m. a month before delivery.

We were anxiously awaiting the day. On 17 April 1930 the baby was born at the Southern Lying-in hospital. I watched the midwife attending her; at the height of her labour the membrane bulged out, causing her great pain. I took an instrument to puncture the membrane. As it was 6 years since I had attended classes in midwifery, I forgot to turn my head away. I got all the water over my head but I was happy because it was our own child's water. In a few minutes the baby emerged. We had all along thought only of a son: we had even talked of him as "Erik". I looked at the newborn baby and was quite taken aback, until I recognized the female organ. Alas, it was a girl, but a big, well-built baby. Brita, coming round, asked, "Is she well formed", and looked very happy when I told her she was. Brita got a cup of coffee and I rushed to tell our family about the happy event. Later in the evening, Brita's youngest uncle, the State Geologist, Dr. Harald Johansson, drank

Yngve and Brita Zotterman with their first-born daughter, Helena, May 1931.

a bottle of wine with me to celebrate the birth of our first child. A month later she was christened Anna Helena Caroline: Anna after her "Mormor" (Mother's mother) and Caroline after her "Farmor" (my mother). She was called Lena, of course, which in Swedish means "smoothly".

At the beginning of 1931 Brita's lovely mother died and shortly after her death her uncle, Harald Johansson, died of pneumonia at the early age of 50. Only a month later our little Lena developed a very bad throat infection with high fever. My colleague, Dr. George Jacobsohn, who lived in the same house, treated her. After a few days she suddenly grew worse; she lay with her eyes closed and large blue spots appeared all over her body. There was no question about the diagnosis: she had septicæmia. It was a terrible thought that we might have a third death in the family – our only child who was so young; I refused to accept it. My friend Dr. Jacob-

State Geologist, Dr. Harald Johansson,
Brita's youngest uncle.

sohn called in his and my former teacher in pediatrics, Professor Isaac Jundell, who came up and examined her and, looking very sadly at me, he said, "There have been some cases who have survived." "I will not accept any other outcome," I said. I heard afterwards that Jundell told his assistants that "The poor father did not grasp how serious the case was." Of course I did, but I refused to give up.

George Jacobsohn was an extraordinarily gifted and experienced practitioner. In 1931 we had no sulpha drugs, no penicillin. There was nothing much to be done except careful nursing. Our friend immediately sent us a young nurse chosen specially – Sister Annie. Lena was in a very poor condition, with a high fever and apparently quite unconscious. But this wonderful nurse managed to feed her and to give her water. It was a tedious job to get her to take it, in small quantities, half a teaspoonful now and then, but she managed it. George Jacobsohn took a quart of blood from Brita and injected the serum into the baby's leg muscles. Whether this treatment or the wonderful nursing was the cause – I suppose a combination of both – but after 10 days Lena suddenly opened her eyes, her temperature dropped and she began to make a full recovery. Professor Jundell was right; even such a grave case of septicæmia may recover to full health (N.B. *when well nursed*). Even today, with all the arsenal of sulpha and antibiotics, such cases are considered grave. Our grateful thoughts often go out to George Jacobsohn and the wonderfully skilled nurse Annie, who both without doubt saved Lena's life.

CHAPTER III

Writing and defending a doctorate thesis. — Night life at Dagens Nyheter. *— A great journalist. — The graduation ceremony in Stockholm's Town Hall, 1933.*

In February 1933 I had written a few chapters of my thesis but I had to collect more and different data for the second half of the paper concerned with the mechanism of "double pain". Finally in March I even brought the Hipp's chronoscope home and performed a last series of reaction time determinations on poor Brita, often waking her in the middle of the night, so the last chapters were written in a great hurry. Brita typed my manuscript and our friend Vilgot Hammarling, now the foreign news editor of *Dagens Nyheter,* Sweden's biggest morning paper, corrected my English. Brita and I often delivered our proofs late at night to the printers, Norstedt & Sons on the North River in the centre of the city. We tried to do so before midnight in order to slip into Rosenbad, the restaurant on the opposite side of the river, where Vilgot and his colleague, the night editor Sigge Berg, used to have supper; after that they could not leave the newspaper until 4 o'clock in the morning. From 1927, for 25 years, I provided this paper with medical and scientific reviews and every autumn I featured the new Nobel laureates in Physiology or Medicine and their scientific achievements, in a special signed column. In those days the professors' collegium, the awarding body consisting of about twenty-five professors, made their final decision at a meeting starting at 8 p.m. Sometimes their bulletin was not issued until 10 o'clock, so the time I had for writing my column was sometimes very short, as the paper went to the printing presses at 1 a.m. and the type-setter had to have the manuscript and

Elsa and Vilgot Hammarling.

portraits before 11.30 p.m. Usually I was prepared – I had my inspired guesses – but sometimes I had not the slightest notion as, for instance, when Nicolle was awarded the prize for his discovery that exanthemous typhoid was spread by fleas. Then I certainly had a couple of hectic hours. But often, when the award was bestowed upon a physiologist or a biochemist, I not infrequently knew the laureate and his work, as when Adrian (1932), Henry Dale and Otto Loewi (1936) and Corneille Heymans (in 1939) received the honour. Sometimes I was even asked to present a feature on them over the Swedish Radio.

Thus I came to know quite a few of the editorial staff of *Dagens Nyheter*, the chief editor of which was Sten Dehlgren, a former Captain of the Royal Navy; the head of the cultural department of the paper was Torsten Fogelqvist, a poet and a writer, one of

42

Captain Sten Dehlgren,   Editor, Ivar Ljungquist.
Editor of Dagens Nyheter.

the eighteen of the Swedish Academy, a most charming, witty and lovable man who spread the warmth of his personality over the whole office. There was also the brilliant executive editor, Ivar Ljungquist, a fine novelist who managed to discipline his large staff very well. There was "Red Top" Nyblom; and "Den Blyge" (The Shy) who occasionally could sufficiently overcome his agoraphobia to visit the editing room at Tegelbacken in the centre of The Klara, the newspaper district of those days. He wrote witty verses several days a week in the social section of the large paper (about 40 pages), the part which most people read. There was also C-E. Holmqvist ("Hqt"), a very efficient news editor who not infrequently called me on the phone about foreign cable news concerning medical or scientific matters. I sometimes looked in at a late hour on my way home from my laboratory on the other side of the bridge across Klara Lake. Although it was their busiest time, they nearly always found a few minutes for a chat.

Editor, C. E. Holmqvist.

Vilgot, as the foreign editor, sat in an adjacent small room by himself, the door always open to the editorial office. Later on he was assisted by the tall and very able K. A. Thunberger, always smiling, even when he was at his busiest. He is now the powerful political editor of *Svenska Dagbladet*. Vilgot Hammarling left the paper before World War II, being appointed press attaché at our Embassy in London, where he proved extremely useful. He restored his connections with the 1917 Club and other left-wing people, friends from his early London years in the 1920s. He married a young English left-wing journalist, Beatrice, who not only bore him two charming sons but also had close connections with the circles who used to throng the Russian Embassy. They lived in London all through the Blitz. One day in the autumn of 1944, when Vilgot was sitting reading a paper on his balcony in Finchley Road, a V:1 missile struck close to his balcony, proceeding only another block before it exploded. Vilgot fainted, but recovered when Beatrice helped him to a double whisky!

Finally in April 1933, 5 weeks before the day allotted for my

Professor Hans Gertz,
Collegium opponent at the disputation, 1933.

thesis, my little book was printed and I rushed to the Decanus of the Medical College, the professor of anatomy, Karl Hesser, who had succeeded my professor, Eric Müller, and handed over the dissertation in accordance with the rules. He turned over the pages of the book, smiled and said: "You know that the Decanus has to examine the dissertation to see that there is nothing indecent in it. Tell me briefly what it is about." "Well," I said, "I believe that I have evidence that there are two kinds of specific nerve fibres mediating pain, one group medullated and another group non-myelinated like the tiny naked sympathetic nerve fibres." He looked at me with kind eyes over the rim of his spectacles and said: "Very good." Then he wrote his approval on the cover of the dissertation, and rang a hand bell. His lab. servant entered and he handed him the little book to be "nailed" on the announcement table at the entrance of the building.

The Collegium had appointed the reader of physiology, Dr. Ernst Abramson, as its opponent. He fell ill, however, having

45

Hugo Theorell, Reader in Medical Chemistry at Uppsala University. The third opponent at the disputation, 1933.

caught a mild scarlet fever (scarlatina) and his duty was taken over by my chief, Professor Hans Gertz, whose principal interest was geometrical and physiological optics. He was also a trained ophthalmologist and kept up a small private practice in his apartment near Stureplan in the centre of Stockholm. He must have been rather shaken by his duty. Already he had urged me to send a copy of the page proofs to his colleague Professor Thunberg at Lund as he was anxious to have the opinion of someone who, even if it was thirty years ago, had once done research on pain.

As was usual, I myself could choose two opponents. As there were no neurophysiologists in Sweden in those days, I went to my senior friend Professor Nils Antoni, head of the Clinic of Neurology. He suggested one of his interns, Sten Lagergren, who agreed to become my first opponent. To serve as my own second opponent I managed to persuade my young friend Dr. Hugo Theorell, at that time reader of medical chemistry at Uppsala University.

Dressed in full evening dress, tails, black waistcoat and white tie, the doctors wearing their pleated silk top hats, I entered, with my opponents, the lecture hall of the pathology building, which had been given a neo-classical decor by the great architect Ragnar Österberg, the famous creator of the adjacent Town Hall of Stockholm.

I went up in to the pulpit. When the clock struck 9.15 the Decanus stood up, turned to the somewhat crowded auditorium and said "With the permission of the Collegium of the Karolinska Institutet med lic. Yngve Zotterman will now defend a thesis" – and, looking down at his copy of my book, he read – "A thesis entitled *'The peripheral nervous mechanism of pain'*. The disputation is opened." Thus he instructed me to defend the thesis, and to act as the chairman of the proceedings.

I started by correcting a few printing errors and then I called upon the opponent of the Collegium, Professor Gertz. Sitting with the other opponents at a small table to the right of me beneath the dais he started giving a summary of the thesis. It took about 20 minutes. He then, as is the rule, asked the defendant (me) whether I approved of his abstract. To the very great astonishment of the audience I replied: "Well, in a way, but it did not relate anything of the leading theme for both parts of my thesis." My opponent grew very nervous, twisted his long moustache and looked rather bewildered, but he started to ask me questions. He went through every page and I did not do so badly, I thought. After nearly 3 hours he arrived at the last chapter where I give my new interpretation of the "double pain." Then he said: "You do not accept Thunberg's theory?" "Of course not," I replied. "But you don't say so, why don't you criticise Thunberg?" "Well," I replied, "why should I? I have quoted his opinion and his evidence for it. Then I give the evidence for my view and let the intelligent reader make his own choice." Then Gertz ended up with a few brief words of congratulation, I went down and shook hands with him and gave him the customary speech of thanks. Gertz was a highly intellectual person, a charming host, he had a great sense of humour (he always had the *Pickwick Papers* at his bedside), but in the lab. he was quite another man. He walked all the way to the Institute every morning – it took half an hour. Arriving at 9.0 a.m., he looked at his notes and gave a lecture from 9.15 to 10. After reading through his rather sparse mail, he then walked home for lunch. In the afternoon he took another walk to and from the lab. and nearly every evening another walk in the east part of the town. I remember Ernst Abramson calculated that he spent nearly twice the amount of time in walking than he spent in the lab. He had been the assistant of old Magnus Blix and he used to tell us that Blix never discussed any of his experiments with anybody else. Gertz's very nervous temperament had hindered him from defending a thesis. He was the only medical professor in Sweden who had no doctor's degree. I believe it must have been because of this difficulty that he never discussed or talked to me about my research. When I thanked him after his opposition I could not resist telling the audience that I was grateful that I had at last, that very morning, after being his assistant for six years, got my first opportunity to discuss my physiological problems with him. This was the truth, but in those days it was considered very improper to say such a thing to a professor, and publicly too. I certainly risked a bad verdict.

I stepped up again into the catheder and according to the rules I asked whether anybody *ex auditorio,* as extra opponent, would like to have the platform. Nobody rose, so I called upon my own first opponent, Sten Lagergren. Poor fellow, he was very young and inexperienced and he had had to wait for more than three hours. His legs had trembled so much that Professor Gertz, himself getting more and more nervous, finally told him to stop his leg from shaking. Lagergren certainly made some quite good points, but after the previous long dialogue I was rather tired. I listened only absent-mindedly to his remarks. When he stopped after about 40 minutes, I called on my second opponent, usually called the *third opponent,* whose duty it is to amuse the audience. He was Hugo Theorell and he certainly entertained us royally, making fun of my thesis and throwing Russian crackers which exploded among the audience, nearly setting Professor Santesson's long white beard on fire. But he also said some words which I appreciated very much, as he ended up by saying "We have all been familiar with Yngve Zotterman, behaving like a fox terrier in the yard of Karolinska Institutet, yapping at all the big dogs, but today we know that he also has the character of a bulldog who does not let go of his grip." (But perhaps he said this in his after-dinner speech in the evening.)

As is the custom, a disputation dinner was given the same night. We had invited the opponents and most of my teachers with their wives to a special reception room. The food was prepared by "Mimma", a wonderful cook; she used to cook for a great number of aristocratic families in Stockholm. There were altogether about sixty people when everybody had taken their seats. I gave a speech of welcome and then gave a toast of gratitude to Karolinska Institutet, to my chief Professor Gertz, to the second opponent, to the third, and finally to Brita and my mother. It was a gay dinner and at the end of the meal the senior professor and the opponents in order gave their after-dinner speeches.

My teacher in biochemistry, Professor John Sjöqvist, and my teacher in surgery, Professor Jules Åkerman, both intimate friends of Brita's Uncle Jöns, were in high spirits. Standing there chatting over the coffee and a cognac, I heard Professor Sjöqvist say to his friend: "Fancy, that fellow Gertz didn't grasp the meaning of the thesis." Unfortunately Gertz was standing just behind him and could not help overhearing. I noticed that Professor Göran

Professor Göran Liljestrand

Liljestrand went over to Gertz and had a long talk with him. What was going on? They were deadly enemies, as Gertz had got the chair of physiology which Liljestrand so badly coveted. He had to take over the department of pharmacology instead. Well, that night Herod and Pilate became friends. I was soon to find out what had been agreed. A few days later I was told that I could not be approved to *docent* in physiology until next term, but with immediate action and without undergoing any exams Liljestrand's own docent in pharmacology was to be appointed docent even though the subject was physiology. Well, there was nothing wrong in this. The Collegium had previously decided that nobody could be a docent in two disciplines in future, but never mind, "pharmacology is what pharmacologists do" Sir Henry Dale once said. (I never saw Liljestrand talk to Gertz again.)

I learned later that they could not give a lower point than two

The fraternities of Stockholm University at the Graduation Ceremony in the Town Hall.

on the thesis, but in order to credit the official opponent Professor Gertz, they gave me only 1½ marks for my defence. All my teachers were by that time retired, so Liljestrand was very powerful, and I was not his pupil.

The following morning I came to give my lecture at 7.30 a.m. at G.C.I. When I reached the platform one of the young men stepped forward and in a few words expressed the good wishes and congratulations of the class, and a young and pretty girl student handed me a beautiful bunch of red roses. They had read about my disputation in the morning papers. Deeply touched and encouraged, I thanked them for their attentiveness in spite of the fact that my teaching that term could not have been inspired, as I was too occupied with my research and in writing my thesis.

Two weeks later I received my doctor's hat, my doctor's ring and my diploma at the great Graduation Ceremony in the Blue Hall of the Town Hall of Stockholm. It is a wonderful ceremony; headed by young students of both sexes carrying the colourful banners of all the different fraternities of the Stockholm Student Groups, the deans, the professors, etc., all in full evening dress and carrying their pleated silk top hats, followed by about fifty *promovendi*, descend in a stately procession from the Prince's Gallery on the first floor down the beautiful stairway of bluegreen Swedish marble and take their seats in front of an audience of about 1500 people, parents, wives, sweethearts and friends of the *promovendi* and the university teachers.

Beneath the stairway, the Academic Orchestra and the student choir conducted by Oskar Lindberg, the composer, played his beautiful cantata to *Alma Mater Holmiensis* for orchestra and choir. The solo was sung by my old friend Seth Svanholm, a brilliant tenor, later often at the Metropolitan Opera and finally director and head of the Stockholm Opera. In the orchestra, I recognized playing the first fiddle my third opponent Dr. Hugo Theorell and quite a few other friends.

After this music one of the *promotors* delivers the promotion lecture, a short lecture on a topic within his field of research given in a way that it can be understood by anyone. Following him the first *promotor,* the Decanus of Karolinska Institutet, which is the oldest University College of Stockholm, starts the promotion of its forty *promovendi.* Most deans perform this in Latin in the customary ancient formula "Ipse, Professor Anatomie in Academia Regensi" etc., putting his doctor's hat on his head. Simultaneously a destroyer on the Riddar Fjord outside the Town Hall fires two guns in salute, *boom, boom!* While the organ up under the high ceiling plays soft music, the *promotor* calls one after the other up the flight of stairs where he declares him doctor and puts the pleated hat on his head, while saying in Latin "Accipe scapula" – *boom!* – and, putting the ring on his left fourth finger, "Accipe annulus aureus" and finally "Accipe diploma" and hands him

"In the hat" after the Graduation Ceremony.

the diploma. The *promoti* now turn round, receive the applause of the audience, proceed slowly down the flight of stairs and then stop and bow to the authorities seated on the first bench, royalties, members of the Government, the University Chancellor, etc.

It is now a lengthy ceremony, as the number of *promovendi* has increased. In the 1930s it only took place every third year, at the end of May. Later it had to be performed each year as the number of *promovendi* increased so much. Anxious to reform university teaching and regulations, the students today have extended their reforming ardour even to the ancient Graduation Ceremony. Thus the promotion ceremony on 30 May 1969 was the last of its kind in the beautiful Town Hall of Stockholm.

When the ceremony is ended there is a subscribed banquet for about 800 people in the Golden Chamber on the first floor. You

53

are given good food, good wine and sometimes, at least, fairly good after-dinner speeches – but perhaps the best of all is the excellent singing by the student choir, conducted by Einar Ralf, a fine composer and singer who never seems to grow older. After dinner we dance in the vast Blue Hall where the students and their girl friends have dined under the arcades and then join us. I wish that all my dear readers could have the opportunity of taking part in such a dinner at Stockholm's Town Hall. It is a magnificent experience.

CHAPTER IV

Adventures as medical officer in the Swedish Navy. — A submarine is missing. — The dangers of deep-sea diving. — A tragedy.

A few years after my national service in the Royal Swedish Navy in the summer of 1918, I enrolled in 1922 as a junior medical officer. At the end of April I was called up to serve as a ship's doctor on H.M.S. *Freja,* an old steam corvette which now was rigged off. It once was one of the biggest ships of the Swedish Navy, having taken King Gustaf V's eldest brother Oscar, later Prince Bernadotte, as far as Constantinople in the 1870s. It was now taken out by tug to the Navy's outpost in the southern archipelago of Stockholm. This took nearly two days. It was cold weather, with snow, and when we anchored the next day, in the bay of the small island of Mäsgarn on 26 April, there was still ice on the fjords. The captain was Egon Ternberg, a very capable

H.M. Steam Corvette Fre j a, 1900.

Brita and the author sailing the quarter boat of H.M.S. Freja, 1922.

officer, and a great sportsman if somewhat eccentric in behaviour. He once rowed a little dinghy from Karlskrona to Gotland. He had to give a large group of sailors doing their compulsory service a military naval training, but he was really using them to build an airport for the naval air force on this small island. It therefore nearly proved fatal to his career when Admiral Wachtmeister came to inspect the ship and found the sailors almost totally ignorant of naval matters.

I cannot resist describing the occasion: the admiral picked out two sailors and ordered them to take their signalling flags. He put them on the deck with a distance between them of about 40 yards. "Now," said the Admiral to the first man. "You will signal this question to your mate," and he whispered a few words in his ear, "And you there," he pointed to his mate, "will signal an answer."

Slowly, with a few mistakes, the first sailor signalled: "What day of the week is it today?" The other fellow stood there motionless. "Can't you read the question?" demanded the Admiral. The fellow nodded. "Well then, answer it," said the admiral. The poor fellow looked very worried at first, but then suddenly he started to signal. I saw Captain Ternberg trying to stifle a laugh. "What is it?" I asked him. "For Heaven's sake," he said. "He is signalling 'Pea soup and pork'." This was a dish served every Thursday to the Navy and Army. I could see the Admiral's little grey moustache starting to twitch and suddenly he burst out laughing and, still smiling, left the deck. I think that this incident saved Captain Ternberg. Sailors, including admirals, generally have a sense of humour.

In the old wardroom of H.M.S. *Freja* I had for shipmates a great number of young officers whom I got to know quite well. We all had our own small cabins with a rather narrow couch to sleep on and little washstands for washing. All the furniture was in beautiful old solid Honduras mahogany, even the doors and wall panels of the wardroom. The officers had their own cooks in their own galley, who provided very good food. At 6 p.m. we all gathered in the wardroom dressed in wardroom jackets, white starched shirts with black tie and patent leather shoes. The youngest officers arrived first, and the captain last of all. He started to serve himself from a rich smörgåsbord, consisting of different kinds of pickled herrings eaten with boiled potatoes, with which you drank a snapps and beer. Then you had some small fried meat balls, or an omelette with stewed asparagus. When the edge of your appetite was dulled you progressed to the big dining table where you were served with soup, a steak or fish, and a dessert. Generally you were attended by a couple of well-trained commissioned waiters. Some of these you might meet later in life as head waiters in big restaurants throughout the country.

The naval officers had a very busy life, which started at 7 a.m.

every morning and often included night duty as well. They were separated from their families, and needed some of the comforts which the wardroom gave them. Like all officers I had a *calfactor*, the junior sick berth attendant, who brushed my uniform, polished my shoes and made my bed, for which duties I paid him a small honorarium. The young men were quite anxious to find such jobs, as they could then save some money for their days on leave and were aware, of course, of the benefits of being an officer's personal servant. It was a gentleman's life on board in the tradition of the ancient Swedish nobility, who dominated the Navy until World War II abolished most of the officer's privileges. In the years when I served on board men-of-war in 1939–42 we dined in plain jackets and ate the same food as the crew, and nobody complained.

My own duty was to attend sick parade every morning at 8 o'clock and treat the patients who were in a small hospital on the island. It was a very easy job, as there were few patients; the ward, accommodating twenty, was quite empty for weeks on end in the summer. The young sailors were healthy and it was only on Mondays that any great number of them appeared on sick parade. Most of them had returned from their long weekend leave, and felt tired, or depressed, complaining of headaches, etc. They usually accepted gratefully a few aspirins and then returned to duty. Once or twice, however, we had an epidemic of mumps. In some cases the patients developed orchitis, with a high fever, and these had to be treated ashore. More serious cases such as appendicitis were sent by ambulance to the military hospital in Stockholm. The same procedure applied to the very few cases of venereal disease which needed specialist treatment. We had a very effective system of prophylaxis in the Navy. Every ship's doctor assembled the crew on the half deck and gave an informatory lecture on venereal disease, its causes, treatment and prophylaxis. I used to warn them that any woman who casually went to bed with a sailor must be looked upon as a potential source of contagion and ended "Do not trust even a Queen". Every man, on return to the ship after casual sexual intercourse, had to go to the sick room and, after registration, get prophylactic treatment. Anybody acquiring V.D., who had not undergone such treatment, had, after being cured, to undergo a week's imprisonment. The system worked very well. I remember that after 3 night's stay by a Swedish flotilla in the port of Tallin in Estonia, 246 prophylactic treatments were given, and during the following month only two cases of V.D. were reported, which was an excellent result.

In 1922 I had to serve for 6 months in H.M.S. *Freja*, but as it took only 1½ hours to drive to Stockholm I quite often visited my mother and Brita.

Some of my shipmates were married or engaged, and we once gave a big dinner party on board for invited ladies. At that time the small hospital happened to be empty so we accommodated our ladies there overnight. Then on the Sunday we took them out to the beautiful archipelago to swim and picnic on the beach.

On other occasions we took the steam-engined ship's boat out on a navigational exercise ending up at Dalarö or Utö where we were warmly welcomed by the ladies from the swimming clubs and danced till a late hour and continued our navigational exercise in the light Swedish summer night. But punctually at 8 o'clock in the morning everyone was on duty.

The life aboard old *Freja* was an idyll, of course, quite different from the hectic life on board the sea-going gunships and destroyers who were in the command of officers making the Navy their career. There the ship's doctor had to train the sick berth attendants and others in the transport of wounded sailors, etc. I did this for a few summers and got quite used to it, and the routine as well. Of course, I complained because I had been in ships every summer in the 1930s, instead of being able to use the vacation for research, as my young colleagues did. Old Uncle Jöns, however, comforted

The author serving at Waxholm Coast
Artillery, Summer 1930.

me by saying, "Don't complain. You have had a wonderful time
with the Navy making friends with so many brave and intelligent
naval officers." He certainly was right. I felt at ease in the company
of my shipmates, although I did not like the feeling of not being
able to leave the ship when you wanted to. But I gradually came
to realize that the regulations were there not just for their own
sake but to make life within a limited space on board a ship
bearable; that they had behind them centuries of experience, and
life was much easier in a well-disciplined ship.

Later on in the 1930s I was for many years on board H.M.S.
Svea, an old gunship built in 1892. Its two 10-inch guns and other
guns were removed and the ship now served as a headquarters
for six submarines. In the large wardroom meals were served for
up to twenty-five officers; the head of the flotilla, a commodore,
dined in the *Kajuta,* having his own galley, with a cook and a

valet. I was selected because I was a physiologist, and had to supervise exercises in escaping from a sunken submarine. A 100-foot high tower was built to train the submarine crews in individual escape, using special breathing apparatus called "lungs". The apparatus was constructed after an American model. Using these "lungs" under water was not without danger to the untrained: if not well instructed, a sailor might hold his breath during the ascent from the base of the 100-foot deep water-filled tower. In this case the compressed air in his lungs expanded and stopped circulation through the lung, or even burst them. In the beginning a few accidents happened in the U.S.A., as well as in Sweden: diving is a dangerous business which requires much practice and knowledge. Even skin-diving has its dangers. Dr. Harald Andersen of Oslo, an expert in the physiology of diving, told me once that he joined a group of twelve young men at La Jolla, California, who were trained in skin diving. After 5 years' experience four of them had met with a fatal accident. In 1940 I visited the U.S submarine base in New London, Connecticut, and I remember the director of the diving research there, Dr. Schilling, who was training sailors to use the tower, told me with deep emotion that he had lost some men. One of them was even an instructor in "free escape", and had made ascents from 120 feet more than a hundred times, but suddenly one day he came up unconscious and died in a few hours. It is extremely sad that, in spite of taking all possible precautions and obeying regulations, man's conquest of the depths has to take such a heavy toll.

In the Swedish Navy we have lost to date no less than ten men in diving practice and research, including the young and promising medical officer, Dr. Berggren, who was doing research in a compression chamber on board H.M.S. *Belos,* the diving ship, when suddenly at high pressure, a window burst. He moved the men to another chamber but was unfortunately too late to save himself, for he acquired the diver's disease, gas bubbles in his veins, and died.

61

H.M.S. B e l o s, the submarine salvage ship of the Swedish navy.

Another fatal accident, which I witnessed myself, was that of a young polytechnic student, Arne Zetterström, a very talented, inventive young man, who had invented new diving devices. In the U.S.A. they had introduced helium gas into deep water diving, in exchange for the nitrogen of the air, for searching greater depths. The advantages of using helium mixtures were several. First, helium is so much lighter than nitrogen that a helium-oxygen mixture at high pressure thus offers much less resistance for the purposes of breathing. Secondly, it was considered that nitrogen under high pressure exercised a narcotic action on the brain. As one had no access to helium at that time (in the 1940s) young Zetterström substituted hydrogen, which is still lighter. But hydrogen and oxygen together is of course "Knallgas", a very explosive mixture. However, Zetterström found out that the mixture is not explosive when the oxygen percentage is kept below 4%, and he suggested that it should be used for diving to great depths. The naval authorities were informed – his father was a prominent ship builder for the Navy – and I was brought in to make experiments with cats in a small compression chamber in the physiology lab. When these experiments proved successful, arrangements were made for deep sea diving. A huge battery of compressed gas mixtures were brought on board the diving ship H.M.S. *Belos,* at the end of World War II, and a successful descent to about 120 metres' depth (about 400 feet) was performed by Zetterström. Breathing the pumped air, he descended to 50 metres, when the air was exchanged to the gas mixture containing 4% oxygen in nitrogen. At this depth the pressure of 4% oxygen was slightly less than the oxygen pressure in atmospheric air at sea level and thus quite sufficient for his needs. Finally this "exchange" gas was exchanged with a hydrogen-oxygen mixture holding only 2% oxygen.

While he was ascending according to an agreed plan, this gas mixture was exchanged to the nitrogen-oxygen gas (4% oxygen) and then to atmospheric air at a certain depth. The ascent became slower and slower as he approached sea level, in order to avoid the dangerous liberation of gas bubbles in the blood or nervous tissues. The rules for such ascents were worked out in the early days of the century by the British Navy, through a commission which had among its active members the eminent Oxford physiologist, John Scott Haldane, and Diving Officer Captain Damant. Using their calculations for step-wise ascents, the risks of diving to depths greater than 30 feet were reduced to a minimum. Commercial divers rarely used to dive to more than 150 feet.

In the summer of 1945 Zetterström made preparations for a world record to descend to a depth of 150 metres (450 feet). I was brought out on the H.M.S. *Belos,* which went out into the deepest water in the Baltic Sea outside Stockholm. Huge batteries of gas containers stood on the deck. Zetterström was dressed in the usual flexible diving suit and put on his helmet, supplied by special valves of his own design. He went into the water, pumps giving him air while he descended. At a certain depth the air was exchanged to the hydrogen-oxygen mixture; he went down to the bottom and reported: "It is lovely, I feel very well." After a few minutes he started to ascend, rather rapidly at first, and then slowly decelerating according to the timetable. He was continually reporting back on the telephone. After a while, however, he repeated the same words again and again and did not answer our questions. Something had gone wrong. Some minutes later some one from the stern shouted: "He is not far below the surface." At that moment he should have been at a depth of at least 200 feet. A diver was sent down, and reported that Zetterström was swimming upside down, at a shallow depth. He was brought unconscious to the surface breathing in gasps, and in a serious condition. He was immediately taken into a compression chamber, which is the only way to treat a case of diver's disease, and brought to a high pressure. There he died, however, without recovering consciousness. It was a horrible accident, and a shock to me; it took me years to recover. I divided my life into two periods, the happy days before this accident and the depressed years afterwards, when I constantly recollected the death of this lovable, brilliant young man. His death was a great loss to deep water diving engineering and to all his friends. I remembered the grief of my mother when my elder brother was drowned in 1913, and I suffered deeply when I thought of Zetterström's parents.

In the spring of 1943 the submarine *Ulven* was reported missing in Skagerack, north-west of Vinga lighthouse. It created great publicity in the papers, and the Navy started a huge project to try to salvage the sub. All kinds of people, technicians, scientists and even "clairvoyants", offered their help. The Navy immediately mobilised a huge flotilla of different vessels covering the area outside the Swedish coast. The head of the Naval medical Corps, Dr. Herbert Westermark, sent me down to Gothenburg, where

64

The Swedish submarine Ulven, sunk by a German mine, 1943.

I was ordered to embark on a salvage vessel, S.S. *Fritiof,* belonging to the Neptun Company. In rather heavy seas we steamed slowly in the area, prepared to send down divers if the sub was located. After three days we anchored at a small jetty. I left the ship, as I did not believe that it could ever be possible to find the sub. I arrived in Stockholm on Easter Thursday and rang up Dr. Westermark: "You should be there on the spot," he said. "It is no use," I said, "there is certainly nobody alive in the wreck, as there are no signals." "Well some Naval officers maintained that they heard knocking signals from the hydrophones at Vinga lighthouse," he said, "although they are not able to decode them, there may be one man alive in the ship, so the Navy has to go on." "But if this is the case, they ought to be able to locate the sub," I said. "Well, it is rather odd," agreed Westermark. Then I had an idea. "Those signals should be recorded," I suggested, "so that we could analyse them." "How can we do that?" he asked. "Well," I said, "I can do it with my cathode-ray oscilloscope." "Wait a moment, give me your phone number, I will call the Admiral and Chief of the Admiralty and telephone you later."

In less than half an hour my phone rang. "You have orders to pack your apparatus and bring it with you at 8 a.m. to the seaplane station at Lindarängen. The plane will bring you to the naval airport outside Gothenburg from where you will be taken on a boat to Vinga." "Very well, Sir," I said, "but I shall need my technical assistant, Mr. Evensen." "All right, bring him too," he replied.

So early on Good Friday morning we took off and two hours later landed outside Gothenburg. Out at Vinga we were helped by some naval people and sea-pilots, who gave us a meal of fresh giant cod, which they had caught the same day. We worked hard rigging up our recording apparatus in a deep grotto in the granite rock. The electrical supply came from a motor driven generator. The next morning, Easter Saturday, 1943, a sister submarine *Draken* was ordered to go out from Vinga and produce signals by knocking with a hammer in the submarine board. We were recording the spontaneous signals thought to come from the submarine all the time, and then the knocking signals given at different distances by the submarine *Draken*. The spontaneous signals were very irregular and did not seem to have any similarity to the very typical knocking signals from *Draken*. We developed several hundred feet of film and after carefully examining them early in the morning of Easter Sunday, I phoned the head of the Gothenburg Naval District, Rear Admiral E. Björklund, to tell him that the spontaneous signals heard in the hydrophones could not possibly come from a man knocking on a sub's board. Further I could calculate that the time for a man to survive in a compartment had now expired as there would be no oxygen left. "Do you realize the seriousness of this report," he asked, "and take responsibility for it?" "Yes," I replied, and he put down the receiver.

66

To be on the safe side, I also called his Chief of the Admiralty, Söderbäck, who was in his office at Stockholm and told him my results. "Thank you very much," he said, "I will now call off the whole salvage fleet. They have taken great risks, because they have been searching an area very close to a large German minefield." So Evensen and I packed up our apparatus. The wife of the Quarter pilot served us a very good dinner: fresh giant cod with melted butter and eggs and potatoes. When we told the master pilot about our recordings he said: "During the last few days we have had huge schools of giant codfishes here, we have caught half a ton of them just outside the island. It could be that their thronging around the hydrophones caused those spontaneous signals." I could not help but agree.

That night we boarded the night train in Gothenburg to Stockholm, accompanied by naval officers, journalists and my old school mate from Vadstena, Sven Jerring, Sweden's principal radio reporter. On the train we heard the news: "Yesterday and to-day thorough investigations of the signals picked up by the hydrophones have been performed by Dr. Zotterman with the assistance of Engineer Svedberg. They have shown that these signals cannot come from the sunken submarine *Ulven*. The head of the Admiralty has therefore called off any further search for the time being."

A few months later the wreck of the *Ulven* was located, finally salvaged and brought in to the Port of Gothenburg. The boat had struck a German mine: the whole crew was instantaneously killed. It was the first and very regrettable loss that the Swedish Navy suffered. I had several friends among the officers and the crew. The captain was the very able and talented Lieutenant Hedelius, recently married to the sweet daughter of a girl who had been my friend from childhood.

The conquest of the sea depths, with that of space, takes its deep toll, but how can you curb the ambitions of man?

CHAPTER V

Further research into skin senses. — "Touch, Pain and Tickle" is published, 1939.

From 1936 to 1938 I worked mainly on the cutaneous nerves of the hind leg of the cat. By dissecting out very fine branches of the nerve I was able to record the response of all the sensory fibres supplying the skin, as this material gave such a favourable signal-to-noise ratio that even the impulses in the tiny C-fibres came through above the noise level. It was wonderful to be able to prove conclusively that pain was mediated by two systems of specific nerve fibres – one relatively fast conducting group of myelinated fibres (Class A:delta) and another group of non-myelinated fibres (Class C) conducting at very low rates. During the same period Herbert Gasser and his associates in the U.S.A., working on large nerve trunks and using electrical stimulation, demonstrated that pain was elicited only when the electrical stimulation was strong enough to excite the delta group of fibres, as well as the C-fibres. In London in 1935 Sir Thomas Lewis and Pochin, working with a group of patients with spinal cord lesions causing a delay of their pain response, and using very much the same method I had described in my dissertation in 1933, found strong evidence that pain in these cases was mediated only by the slow C-fibres. But in addition I made a few other observations which were not of less interest. Mechanical stimulation of the skin produced not only large spikes from the largest fibres, but also from the delta and C group. When further analysing the response to different mechanical stimulation, I found that a very light touch with a fine brush elicited, particularly when repeated, a long volley of very small spikes most likely deriving from C-fibres. I therefore concluded that C-fibres must be involved in the nervous

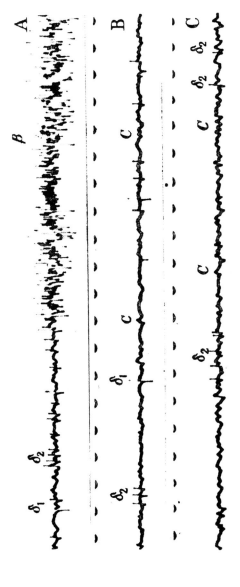

Records of nerve impulses from a fine branch of a cutaneous nerve of the cat in response: (A) to a firm stroke with a wooden pin; (B) from the same record 3 seconds later; (C) light burning. Time 1/50 second. To be read from right to left. (Zotterman, 1938.)

69

mechanism of superficial tickle. These fibres must end very super-
ficially in the skin, as was later demonstrated by anatomists like
Weddell in Oxford. Let us try an experiment together. Move
the tips of the fingers of the right hand very lightly over the palm
of your left hand and repeat this procedure – very lightly touching
the palm! – and you will experience a tickling sensation. Sometimes
it may reach such a height of sensation that you want to scratch
the skin. Please do so! Scratch the palm with your nails. And now
repeat the stimulus. It no longer produces a tickling sensation
because the very superficial nerve endings responding to such a
light and repeated touch were damaged by your scratching. After
about 20 minutes they will rearrange themselves and respond to the
tickling stimuli.

These endings are very easily damaged by all kinds of rough
handling of the skin. In a lecture once at Worcester, Massachusets,
I mentioned that squirting hot water on the skin inhibited tickle,
and a gentleman in the audience got up and said: "Don't you
really mean that you can't tickle a hot one?" (It was the late
Dr. Gregory Pincus, the famous specialist on sexual hormones,
who invented the contraconceptive pill, who gave me this story
to use in lectures.)

I understood that the sensation tickle thus had to be looked
upon as a special sensory modality conducted in its specific nerve
fibres, just as are cold, warmth, pressure and pain. I realized
that the mechano-sensitive system of the skin was much more
differentiated than had been previously realized, as different kinds
of mechanical stimulation gave rise to quite different sensations.
Alrutz, a psychologist at Uppsala, had already in 1901 suggested
that tickle was mediated by a special kind of nerve and his intuition
might prove to be correct.

The years before World War II were very stimulating ones.
My friend, Olof Sjöqvist, the son of my biochemistry professor,
had returned from a few years sojourn as house surgeon in the

Dr. Olof Sjöqvist, neurosurgeon, 1954.

provinces to assist Herbert Olivecrona, who pioneered brain surgery in Sweden. Olle Sjöqvist, who was our dear friend, became very interested in my pain research. One night I suggested that he should consider how different nerve fibres run in the roots of the trigeminal nerve, the sensory nerve supplying the face. Perhaps the small myelinated and the C-fibres run into a separate tract in the brain stem as they do in the spinal cord. Thus by cutting them you might block the pain in cases of trigeminal neuralgia without producing facial anæsthesia, i.e. the patient will not feel pain, but will still respond to touch and pressure – a great improvement on the previous method of operation, when the face became insensitive and felt dead.

Sjöqvist went to the histology department and started his research on the roots of the nerve. After some months he found that the largest fibres turn upward in a special tract when entering the brain stem, while the small fibres run downwards into the cervical

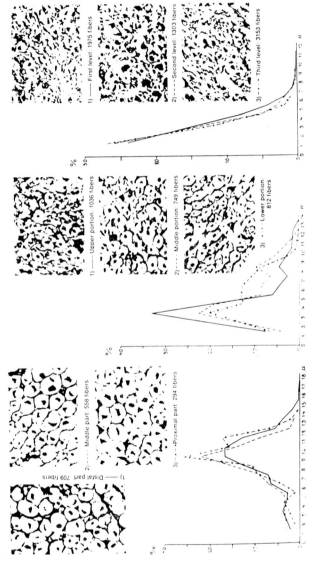

(A) Diagram and microphotos showing the fibre size of the myelinated fibres in the trigeminal motor root. (B) Diagram and microphotos of nerve fibres in the trigeminal sensory root near the pons. (C) Diagram and microphotos of nerve fibres in the spiral trigeminal tract. (O. Sjöqvist, 1938.)

region where they cross over. He thus decided to enter with his knife in the lower part of the brain stem at the height of a nucleus called the *olive* and cut these small trigeminal nerve fibres. He did this on a patient suffering from severe trigeminal neuralgia, with terrible pain in the lower half of the face and cheek. The operation was performed while his chief was on leave and when Olivecrona returned Sjöqvist was able to demonstrate the result with great pride. The pain had gone and the lower part of the face was quite insensitive to painful stimuli, but responded to touch and pressure. Further examination revealed that the sensation of temperature was also impaired. In a period of a few months Olle Sjöqvist operated on another two patients – and his chief more still – and in 1937 Sjöqvist defended his thesis on this new operation for trigeminal neuralgia (now called "Sjöqvist's Tractotomy") which made him famous throughout the world of neurosurgery, a new, rapidly growing discipline.

I had another interest in these cases. I managed to make a sensory study of a few cases operated on by Sjöqvist's method. I asked them to shut their eyes. Then I touched the skin on the lips and on the cheek on the operated side. They correctly reported "yes" each time I touched the face, and even when I pricked the skin with a needle, but reported no pain nor any response to cold or heat on that side, in contrast to the other side. All this was to be expected. But then I touched one patient lightly on the nose with a wisp of cotton wool on one side. His face twitched: "It tickles," he said. I applied the same stimulus to the other (operated) side, and there was no twitching. The patient correctly reported every touch and then said: "It's funny, I can't be tickled on this side of my face any longer." I obtained identical results in the other cases. Thus the operation had cut off not only the pain and temperature fibres from the face, but also the *tickle* fibres. This proved, I thought, that tickle is mediated by fibres which run in the same tracts as pain and temperature but quite separately from the larger sensory fibres mediating touch and pressure.

I reported all these findings at the International Physiology Congress in Zürich in August 1938 in a paper called "Touch, Pain and Tickle" which I sent to the *Journal of Physiology* in England where it appeared in 1939. It was not a bad paper, I thought, although at that time, like Erlanger and Blair in the U.S.A., I believed that the conduction rate of myelinated fibres varied with the square of the diameter. It was soon definitely proved it was a linear function. It did not, however, affect my main results and Gasser became very interested. I was acting as secretary to the chairman, who was Adrian, in a section of the proceedings which contained papers by Adrian on the labyrinth, Hartline on single optic nerve fibres, Sand on his discovery that the Lorenzian ampulla of fish is a sensory organ reporting cooling, and my own paper. I was proud of being in such fine company. After my paper, Gasser beckoned me down from the platform and said: "Let's get out of here," and we went outside and discussed my paper for several hours in the garden. Gasser, who was then the young new director of the Rockefeller Institute, was not easy to convince, as he did not believe it was possible to record from single C-fibres. But he was finally convinced and in a report in 1942 he gave me full credit for being the first to suggest that pain was mediated by these tiny fibres. In the same paper Gasser suggested that the tiny C-fibres may mediate other sensations as well, particularly cold and warmth. Many years later Ritchie and Douglas, developing quite an ingenious method applying both electrical and natural stimuli to cutaneous nerve trunks, made it seem very likely that light mechanical stimulation excited even C-fibres, thus confirming my direct findings in the 1930s. Not being sensory physiologists, however, they did not relate their findings to superficial tickle. Douglas, quoting my earlier papers, denied me the right of classifying the spikes in my records as C-spikes as I had not determined their rate of propagation. With

74

my long experience in recording spikes from single sensory fibres I could quite easily classify the fibres by comparing the relative spike heights and the configurations of the record and none of today's specialists, like Professor Ainsley Iggo at Edinburgh, would deny that already by 1935 I had recorded impulses from single C-fibres.

It had taken me a long time to achieve it; I had lost many years but I was hunting big game. We know now that about 80–90% of all sensory fibres supplying the skin are non myelinated fibres all very highly specific although they do not show any specific end-organs – at least not under the light microscope. They subserve particularly tickle, pain, cold and warmth – in general sensations which have an emotional character. The great English neurologist, Sir Henry Head, once divided the sensory nerves into two groups, epicritic and protopathic. The sensory fibres of the C-class would thus belong to the latter group – the protopathic. In the spinal cord as well as in the brain stem these run in specific pathways to the *thalamus,* the last large relay station below the cerebral cortex. On their way to the thalamus, however, they send collaterals into a central mass of relays within the brain stem, the *reticular system,* which in its turn signals to the cortex, keeping the cortex awake, as was discovered in the late 1940s, by Magoun and Moruzzi. Pain and tickle are particularly efficient in arousing and keeping the brain awake, because they have such a rich system of collaterals running into the reticular system.

Lord Adrian, my master and friend, once wrote to me, "I accept the existence of specific tickle fibres, but what is the purpose of specific tickle receptors in the skin?" "Well," I replied, "if you go into a stable you will see how the horses' manes and tails are continuously moving, reflexes elicited by the slightest mechanical stimulation, by the touch of an insect. The sensory functions of the skin developed during the millions of years that we, like other mammals, lived in a world of insects."

I ought to stop talking about tickle now, but I cannot resist telling you that at the last International Physiology Congress in August 1968 in Washington D.C., Dr. Burgess and Dr. Perl from Salt Lake City reported that they had developed a new technique for recording from single cutaneous sensory nerves which makes it very easy to study the function of even the smallest of fibres. Instead of splitting up the nerves they enter the cell bodies of the tiny nerve fibres in their posterior root ganglia with a micro-electrode of about 0.001 millimetres at the edge. The cell body is generally of a diameter 6–7 times as big as the nerve fibre. Thus even the smallest fibres – 0.0005 millimetres – have a cell body of 0.0030 millimetres in diameter enabling them to enter with a fine electrode. They found an abundant number of C-fibres which responded very specifically to a tickling stimulus like a fly walking over the skin. It is like a very sophisticated land mine, which does not explode when one man walks over it, but when the third or fourth man passes. I shall never forget that when I left the lecture theatre in Washington after Burgess's and Dr. Perl's review of the results which the Salt Lake City School had obtained, Dr. Pat Wall with whom I have had so many hot but friendly disputes in the last 20 years said to me: "Yngve, you must be quite content at last, now all your findings and theories have been finally confirmed." That was indeed generous of him.

CHAPTER VI

Teaching physiology to gymnast students, 1930-40.

In 1929 my senior colleague, Dr. Ernst Abramson at the Physiology lab. was appointed laborator in physiology at the Karolinska Institutet. He handed over the teaching of physiology, school hygiene and gymnastic theory in the Central Institute of Gymnastics to me in 1930. Although rather elementary work, there was nevertheless a lot to do. For 8 months of the year I had to deliver eighteen lectures a week. Five days a week I rushed to the old building on the Brunkeberg Hill in Hamngatan to start a double lecture at 7.30 in the morning. Only once in 11 years did I oversleep, thanks to Brita, who generally woke early with the children.

On the first floor in an old rectangular lecture room, heated by four huge porcelain stoves in each corner, forty young girls and twenty young men awaited me. How they kept awake I do not know, because I am sure I was a very poor lecturer, at least for the first year, when I had to read my lectures from manuscript. Some of the girls were knitting, which Abramson had allowed them to do, preferring that to their chattering. There were three classes: the first year and second year, to which I taught physiology and general gymnastic theory; and to the third year I gave special gymnastic theory and school hygiene. Most of the young men were officers from the Army and Navy who attended for only one year. The third class consisted only of about twelve students. I met many of them afterwards – fine-looking women who have kept their good carriage and look very fit and healthy. Most of them are married and are employed at high schools teaching physical education. Some have left their profession, like Inga Thorson, our former ambassador to Israel, and Gudrun Friberg, the wife of

Sten Friberg, professor of orthopædics and the rector magnificus of the Karolinska Institutet.

They were altogether a most happy student body. At least twice a year they arranged parties to which they invited their teachers. Usually it was a dinner party at a restaurant. After dinner, which started with snapps and smörgåsbord followed by a main course and wine, the students gave a *spex* with songs and jokes at the expense of their teachers. As I used to do demonstrations on frogs' nerve-muscle preparations, they could not resist making up verses about the frogs jumping out between my lips during my lectures. Gudrun Friberg was a charming sight when she came on the stage in full evening dress, tails and white tie and with an opera hat just like Ginger Rogers in "Top Hat". Had she taken lessons from her brother Tor Modéen, who was at that time Sweden's most popular comedian? I suppose they were both gifted in this way. Afterwards we danced until closing time – 2 a.m. We mostly danced modern dances, the one-step, tango, etc., but quite frequently did Swedish barn dances as well, as they were going to teach these dances to school children. So we danced the hambo, originally introduced in Sweden from Poland in the sixteenth century, when Sigismund, grandson of the first Wasa king, was also the King of Poland. This dance is particularly popular in Dalecarlia. Brita, who was brought up in Rättvik, at the great lake Siljan at Dalecarlia, had taught me to dance the special form of Rättvik's hambo where you mark with a step every fourth note in the three-quarter rhythm. So we, as we still do to this day, danced the Rättvik hambo while the others danced the more usual curtseying hambo, where the couple bend down while swinging round. A strong man ends every series of this dance by lifting his girl as high in the air as he is able to.

We had a very good time with the young gymnasts who were barely 10 years younger than me. Some of the naval officers had been my shipmates during summers I spent as a medical officer

78

on board different naval vessels, mostly submarines. As we met almost every day, we got to know each other well. I have only happy memories of those 11 years in the 100-year-old building erected by the great Per Henrik Ling as a seminary for teachers in physical education in order to improve the poor physical condition of the Swedish people.

Until the turn of the century the G.C.I. was the leading centre of gymnastics in the world. A great number of its alumni of both sexes emigrated and started gymnastic institutes abroad, in Germany, England, France, South America – all over the world. There they practised in medical gymnastics and massage. These "Gymnastikdirektors", as they were called, were exceedingly prosperous and acquired patients from high society, titled and noble persons. The men were generally former officers, handsome, tall fellows and their women colleagues educated daughters of good Swedish families. They were all well trained and conducted themselves well. These successful Swedish gymnasts had given Sweden a worldwide reputation from which quite a few of my pupils were able to profit.

Until 1912, when the Swedish gymnastic troupe won the gold medal at the Olympic Games at Stockholm, G.C.I., under the good guidance of the Directors, like Branting, Balk and Drakenberg, successfully upheld its national and international reputation. Swedish medical gymnasts were also very successful, during and after World War I, in treating disabled soldiers in France, Germany, Great Britain and the U.S.A. At home, however, several competitive gymnastic systems developed, some of them influenced by ideas from the Danish Gymnastic School where the teaching was in the hands of an eminent physiologist, Professor Lindhard. He had written two books: *General Gymnastic Theory* and *Special Gymnastic Theory,* which were introduced by Abramson as text books for the second and third classes respectively. In these books Lindhard made a brilliant analysis of the physiological effects of the different gymnastic movements. He criticized the orthodox Ling's gymnastics for women, which he found unnatural, and pleaded for a more relaxing and natural system of gymnastics for women which had been introduced in Copenhagen. The ancient Ling's system, which had been looked upon as sacrosanct (although its rigidity had been introduced by Ling's successors), was fiercely defended by most of the old gymnastic directors, and Abramson was looked upon as a heretic when he introduced new ideas as a member of the board.

The buildings in Klarabergsgatan were old and dark, and completely derelict. For decades one committee after the other had written long reports advocating new buildings and a reorganization of the teaching, but nothing was done. In 1927, my teacher Professor Johansson resigned as chairman of the Board, as did all its members, in protest against the inactivity of the Government, which at that time was a Conservative one with Professor Lindskog as head of the Department of Education. Finally in 1948 the Government decided to move the G.C.I. into new buildings to be constructed on a site close to and north of the Olympic Stadium of Stockholm. The teaching was completely reorganized, the medical gymnastics were separated and entirely taught at the Karolinska Hospital, and a special department of physiology, headed by a professor, was planned. The post of Professor was given to Dr. Erik Hohwü Christensen, a son of South Jutland, an eminent expert physiologist on muscular exercise, a former pupil and excellent co-worker of Lindhard and August Krogh in Copenhagen. Under his guidance there has been a great development of the old G.C.I., now called Gymnastik- och Idrottshögskolan G.I.H (Gymnastic and Athletic High School). Professor Christensen has made his own prominent researches into athletics and in industrial physiology. When he resigns in 1970 he has every reason to be content, as he has fulfilled a most important task, that of making expert physiologists out of so many gymnasts.

CHAPTER VII

A grand tour of Europe, 1937. — Hitler's Berlin. — Happy days in Vienna, Budapest and Venice. — An awkward silence.

In the spring of 1937 Brita and I were able to make a grand tour of Europe, ending up in England, thanks to a Retzius travelling fellowship from the Medical Society of Sweden. We went by train to Hitler's Berlin on 29 April in order to visit the Kaiser Wilhelm Institute for Brain Research at Buch, about 8 miles east of Berlin. The Nazis celebrated 1st May with an enormous quantity of red flags bearing the Swastika and huge banners with such devices as "Ohne Sozialismus Kein Nationalsozialismus" (Without socialism no national socialism) on every second house. Loudspeakers placed in the trees reverberated everywhere in the avenues and in the parks, and you heard the voices of Hitler, Goebbels and others speaking for hours on end. Perhaps it is inaccurate to say that Hitler spoke; he cried, he threatened, he exploded. Goebbels was by far the best speaker. When Hitler was heard over the loudspeakers on 1st May the people stood stretching up their right arms in the Nazi salute. I saw an old man standing for half an hour, as if in a trance, listening intently as though to God. He was so tired that he had to use his left arm to support his stretched-out right arm. It was a pitiful sight. We met a few relatives of Brita's uncle, Professor Ernst Riesenfeld, who wisely had left Germany by 1932. His cousin Dr. Friedländer, previously secretary to Fürst Lichnovsky, the German Ambassador to London before the days of Hitler, took us out in his motor car so we saw a lot of Berlin and its surroundings. Dr. Friedländer was one of the last Jewish people who were able to leave Germany – illegally of course.

He managed to avoid being sent to any concentration camps. Deliberately he made an illegal financial transaction which brought him into an ordinary prison and after a year, when he had served his term, he managed to reach Switzerland and from there he could proceed via Cuba to the U.S.A. He was a tall, very handsome and courageous man, a great German patriot, who did not want to leave his fatherland until it became absolutely unbearable to live there any more.

At Berlin-Buch we were very cordially received by Dr. Kornmüller, who was one of the very first to use Berger's discovery of the electrical brainwaves to study the activities of the brain. He had been discovered by the former head of the institute, Professor August Vougt, the famous brain research worker. He was no longer there, because Hitler did not approve of the fact that he was called to Lenin's sick bed in Russia. His successor was Professor Spaatz, a Bavarian pathologist, who was particularly interested in diseases of the basal ganglia of the brain. He had collected twenty severe cases of chorea major. His poor patients suffered from involuntary movements; suddenly an arm is lifted up, or the head jerks aside, and so on. I followed him on his rounds. It was a strange experience to walk with him through this ward, the patients standing at the foot of their beds on either side of the room exhibiting these involuntary movements; arms are suddenly raised, heads turn to the side, legs are kicked – a very grotesque spectacle. But when we left the ward, we met a group of twelve young nurses marching along the corridor. When they saw Professor Spaatz their right arms automatically shot up as they cried "Heil Hitler"!

Aloïs Kornmüller showed me his fine equipment made by Dr. Jan Friedrich Tönnies. He had constructed a balanced input amplifier, which was very useful for neurophysiologists. His design of ink-writers for recording the brain-waves (EEG, electroencephalogram) which are of relative low frequencies compared to the spikes which I recorded, made it possible to follow the course of events on the recording paper.

There was also the Russian-born geneticist Timoteef Resovsky. He was a tall, strongly built man with a big fine head covered by a great mane of grey hair. Using hard X-rays, he brought about genetic mutations; his research was very well known. He was of a lively, intellectual disposition, openly denouncing the regime of "these brown-booted fellows behind an engine, more or less idiots, who believe that they became great by making as much noise as possible".

Most of the scientists I met in Berlin-Buch gave me the impression of being unhappy. Some of them were quite aware that they were heading for a war. They also had a feeling of being watched by Nazi party members, particularly those who had been brought there by August Vougt and his Frenchborn and scientifically active wife.

After a few days in Berlin we took the train to Prague. We saw but a few of our Czech colleagues but we were very kindly received by old Professor Zeissenegg-Tshermak at the German-speaking university. We went into his huge office on the first floor of his laboratory. Tables, chairs and window sills were covered by books, reprints and manuscripts piled on top of each other. Behind similar piles on an enormous writing desk a huge head shot up, with long white hair, a moustache and a beard like the Emperor Franz Josef. He rose, and lifted a pile of books from two chairs down onto the floor so that we could sit down, talking continuously and giving us details of the physiological problems which he was investigating. After about an hour, his lab. man entered to tell him that his class was waiting in the lecture hall, and offered him on a silver tray a glass of port wine, which he gulped down in one draught, and rushed off to his lecture.

Later on we visited the Czechoslovakian university where we met a group of young men who apparently were very active, although their equipment seemed to be rather sparse. A few of them had been to the U.S.A. and England and preferred to speak English with us. They were, of course, Czechoslovakian nationalists, very frightened by the aggressive policy of the Nazis in Germany and the Sudetan provinces of old Bohemia. They had every reason to be.

We stayed in a hotel in the middle of the old city and enjoyed strolling around looking at the medieval buildings in the narrow streets. We crossed the river on the ancient and beautiful bridge in the middle of which a sign informed us that it was here the Bohemians in 1648 had beaten the Swedish Army and thrown them out of the town.

We were served a good supper at a nice little wine restaurant on a terrace below the Palace Hradcany. The view over the city was magnificent in the full moon. A middle-aged blonde lady sitting at an adjacent table smiled at us and started to tell us in German the names of the churches, etc. When we had finished she offered to act as our guide, and we followed her up the narrow paths to the Palace, the residence of Dr. Benes, the President. We entered into the famous Astrologer's street, everybody we met saluting our guide – who was the matron of the President's laundry. She told us a lot of stories about the ancient buildings and even entered into more recent court gossip, which I have now forgotten. Like all Czechs she was very devoted to Benes, who was certainly a great man. It was a very pleasant evening, but somehow rather melancholy, because you did not need to be a prophet to realize that Czechoslovakia was in great danger.

The following night we went to hear Lucienne Boyer singing *Parlez moi d'Amour* in her special French way. We proceeded to a cabaret where I remember we saw something rather startling – a very athletically built lady acrobat in black tights with gold strips ascended the trapeze and there, hanging downwards by her toes, she sang an operatic aria. When that was finished she came down on the stage and played a trumpet solo. She must have been Olympia in Eric Linklater's amusing novel, *Don Juan in America*.

Next afternoon we arrived at Vienna, where we met Brita's cousin Ester Arrhenius, who, having a good singing voice, studied phoniatric with the famous Professor Fröschl. Vienna had not been able to regain its pre-war splendour but life was much more easy. The Wieners had not lost their famous, characteristic humour. The scientific laboratories were old and badly equipped, but the intelligent and ambitious young assistants were carrying on although very badly paid and lacking guidance. You could not blame the Professors for this. They were extremely badly paid too and had enormous teaching and examination burdens, the number of students increasing heavily, and they were very conscientious about their teaching.

One night Ester Arrhenius brought us out to Grinzing, a city renowned for its Weinstübl and Weingartens. We went into a place "wo es ausgesteckt war", i.e. where they put up over the entrance an announcement that they are opening a new barrel of wine. We entered several of these small inns, sampled their wines and had a gay time singing the old songs. Most places provided professional singers and musicians of both sexes. The singers were frequently patients in Fröhlich's phonetic clinic, where Ester had treated them. When she entered they bowed and saluted the pretty blonde Swedish girl, and coming down to our table afterwards said, "Tomorrow, Fräulein Arrhenius, we will come to the clinic." They were generally quite good artists, but they were of course badly paid, having to rely almost entirely on what the guests put on the plate. Some of them were so good that we felt ashamed to tip them. The charming Wiener songs like "Sag beim Abschied leises Servus" from the film *Burgtheater*, still ring in my ears as I write these lines.

While all these songs were in major keys, there were some

unmistakable notes in a dark minor key in the general atmosphere in Vienna in the spring of 1937. There were quite a few young men at the university who were infected by the Nazi ideas about Anschluss and the Austrian Government was in a difficult position, with Hitler in the north and Mussolini in the south. I still feel sorry for these young idealists; they would later deeply regret their enthusiasm. They paid a terrible price.

Our next stop was Budapest, where at the station we were met by our Hungarian friend and colleague, Aladar von Beznak, whom we had got to know in Cambridge and in London in the 1920s. He had recently been appointed Professor of Physiology at the Medical Faculty of the University and introduced to us his wife Margit, a young and keen former student of his. They took us to their apartment in the basement of Villa Verez, on the top of the hill on the western side of the Danube. It was a fine red-brick building belonging to the Minister of Finance (the Hungarian word *ver* means blood, Villa Verez is thus the red villa) where we stayed with them for a happy week.

The following morning they woke us up at 6 a.m. and after having some tea they took us down to their lab., where we arrived punctually every morning at 7 o'clock. It was an institute which was full of life. Aladar von Beznak had been well trained in Cambridge and brought with him the English way of administering science. He had a large group of intelligent and ambitious young research workers of both sexes. He also had time to write a big physiology textbook in Hungarian. It looked very much like its English prototype, Starling's textbook, and it was more up to date than any other textbook of its kind on the European continent.

We spent most of the day in the laboratory. At 12.30 p.m. there was a plain but good meal served in the tea room, which was a very unusual room. Beznak had brought in some rustic provincial peasant women who had covered every square inch of the walls with painted flowers in different colours, giving a most wonderful and artistic effect.

After lunch the Beznaks returned to their apartment and went to bed for two hours, for the siesta, and returned at 3.30 p.m. to their lab., which they did not leave until 8 or 9 p.m.

While they were having their siesta, we took the opportunity of looking around the city. Our hosts liked to go to bed early, at 10 p.m., but one night they took us to the opera where we saw the Hungarian operette *Madame Szibill* by Kálmán, which was very well performed. Afterwards we tried to invite them to go with us to one of the famous night clubs and listen to the well-known gipsy bands, but they gasped with horror and we went straight back to bed.

One day I asked Aladar to bring us to see Georg von Békésy, an electrical engineer who at that time was working in the research laboratories of the Hungarian Telegraph and Telephone Department some 10 miles east of Budapest. I had read quite a few of his papers on acoustics in a new German journal *Zeitschrift für Akustik* and my young colleague in Uppsala, Ernst Bárány, had used his ingenious methods in studying the acoustic properties of different parts of the ear. He was surely a *connaissance à faire*. He was then 35, and spoke German with a broad Swiss accent, having been brought up in Switzerland, where his father was the resident minister of the Austrian-Hungarian Embassy at Berne. He had graduated from the Eidgenössige Technische Hochschule at Zürich. He showed us around in his lab. where he had developed and invented ingenious methods for studying the acoustic physical properties of musical instruments; and from our conversation it emerged that he was going to apply these new methods in research on the human ear-drum and the cochlea of the inner ear.

He showed us some very simple methods of producing pure sinus waves of very low frequencies, down to 0.5 Hz and we had a most interesting day with him. When I got back home I told

Gunnar Holmgren, Professor of Otology, about Békésy and this resulted in my writing to invite Békésy to go to Stockholm to lecture to the otologists as well as to our Physiological Society in Stockholm. Thus Békésy's great contributions to otology were recognised in Sweden before he was appointed as professor of physics at Budapest University, from which chair he came to Sweden in 1947 for a year and then proceeded to Harvard University in the U.S.A. Békésy is in many respects a very unusual person. He gives an impression of being shy and ascetic but he is not. He is a brilliant speaker in a quiet way with a very great sense of humour. He is one of the most cultured men I have ever met, with a vast experience and knowledge of science, art, music and even of cookery.

In 1947, when he worked with me for some time in my lab. at the Veterinary School in Stockholm, we got to know him quite well. He often dined with us in our house at Experimentalfältet. Our Finnish cook took a special interest in him, as Finns and Hungarians belong to the same Finnish-Ugrean language group. One night she laid out the cards for him (Finnish women are good at this) and to his great amusement and to ours too she told him that he would soon marry and have four children. A prediction which did not come true, as Georg von Békésy is still a bachelor.

We took a sleeper and passing through a strip of the Kingdom of Serbia in the night, we woke up the next morning in Steiermark and got out of the train in Graz. It is an old city with beautiful ancient buildings in the Italian style. We paid a visit to Otto Lœwi who received us very kindly. The Lœwi family lived in a very fine house surrounded by a beautiful garden. We had met him for the first time in Stockholm in 1926 when he demonstrated his discovery of the *Vagusstoff* in the heart when the vagus nerve was stimulated. He had been able to prove that this transmitter liberated in the endings of certain nerve fibres was identical with acetylcholine, a discovery which gained him the Nobel Prize in

1935. We had spent 13 days together on the SS. *Minnekahda,* sailing from England to Boston in 1929, so it was a hearty reunion. We were invited to a *Mittagessen* in their very tastefully furnished house, where Frau Lœwi served us an excellent meal, giving us among other things a generous helping of fresh boiled asparagus, with melted butter and bread crumbs. I remember this because we did not eat it as at home, with our fingers, nor with a knife and fork but with small silver forceps about half an inch wide, looking like the bill of a duck. It was a most useful implement which I have never seen before or since.

I spent the next morning in Lœwi's lab., a huge institute of pharmacology. The recent Nobel laureate had a large group of assistants. I followed him from room to room as he went on his daily rounds. Otto Lœwi was a very vivacious character. He looked at the sooted paper records on the kymograph and listened to his assistant's report, constantly interrupting him by loudly expressing either his approval or misgiving. "Why didn't you do as I told you?" he would say with an air of disappointment. After a few words of explanation from the unfortunate assistant he suddenly jumped in the air, literally exclaiming: "Fine, that's excellent, young man, go on!" This went on for several hours. He was a fantastic person, with his enthusiasm and histrionic manner. After some hours, he took me for a walk, and climbed the 700-foot hill in the centre of the town, from where we had, of course, a fine view over Graz and its surroundings. There were a great many delightful squirrels which Lœwi enjoyed feeding with hazel nuts which he brought in his pocket on his daily walk up to the top of the hill. Lœwi was a delightful person, in the prime of his life. A few years afterwards he had to buy himself out of Graz with his Nobel prize money from Sweden. He finally reached the U.S.A. where I met him a few times. He was by then an old man, but still scientifically active and his enthusiasm for his field of research

The marble lions before the Arsenal in Venice.

was unchanged. On my last visit to his apartment in New York his heart was failing, and he died a few months later in 1965.

We left Graz early one morning on the train to Venice. It was a wonderful tour through the Alpine valleys. We were speechless at the beauty of the scenery as the train puffed down the steep valley to the Venetian plains. At the station we managed to get a gondola which took us through the Canale Grande out on the lagoon, landing us at a small hotel, Bucciatore, not far from the naval arsenal. Our room was on the top of the Navy's Chapel. The next morning we were wakened by a large marine orchestra playing outside the church. We had some wonderful days in Venice, visiting all the beautiful places, swimming at the Lido and enjoying the good *table d'hôte*. The currency was very favourable for us and half a litre of wine per person was always included in the price of the meal.

One day we visited the Arsenal where they had a fine Naval museum. On each side of the entrance there are the high marble lions which the Venetians while fighting the Turks in the seventeenth century, brought home from the port of Pireus in Greece. On the back of one of the lions there is a garland of runic letters cut into the white marble. This inscription derives no doubt from a Viking who had by way of the Russian rivers reached "Mikla-gord" – Constantinople – where so many Swedish vikings served in the East Roman Emperors' guard. You may remember that the inscription on the big rune stone at Högby, east of my native town Vadstena, tells of a certain Gulle who had five sons. One of these, so the rune says, died in Miklagord. The Swedish soil has also given lots of coins and gold of East Roman origin brought into the country during the tenth century.

The leader of the Venetian army against the Turks was Field Marshal Königsmark, the brother of the great beauty Aurora Königsmark, the mistress of King August der Starke of Saxonia. We read in school how she tried to charm our young war-lion King Karl XII, who, however, was never interested in women. A pity perhaps, as his energies could perhaps have been led to other activities than the wars which finally ruined Sweden. But on the other hand we may be grateful that he disposed of Sweden as a great power more than 250 years ago. It was Königsmark who was responsible for the damage to the Parthenon on Acropolis. The Turks used the temple as a gunpowder store.

We had reluctantly to leave Venice, and proceeded via Munich and Würzburg to Heidelberg. There we lived in the Schloss Hotel high up above the ruins of the old castle, with a most wonderful view out over the town and the Neckar valley. We had arranged with Dr. Friedländer in Berlin that he should send us money-"frozen money" – belonging to Brita's uncle Professor Riesenfeld, which he was not allowed to take outside Germany. We asked for a registered letter every morning but the porter only shook his head. He was a very nice old man, however, and every morning he lent me 50 marks so that we could get about. Brita became very nervous about this and after a week I finally approached the hotel director in his office and told him about our financial situation. "Oh," he said, "I received 1000 Marks a week ago from

Berlin. Now I understand it is for you." So we went to the kind porter, paid him back his money and thanked him very heartily. He smiled and thanked me, accepting my quite substantial tip.

In Heidelberg I paid a visit to the physiology lab. in the old institute once administered by the great Helmholtz who invented his retinoscope and other ingenious apparatus and formulated his fundamental theories for hearing and colour vision before he was appointed to Berlin's university as professor of physics. The physiologist in charge was now Professor Achelis, a pupil of the neurophysiologist Gildemeister of Leipzig. Achelis had joined the Nazi Party early on and advanced to a post as under-secretary for state in the Ministry of Education. He was a tall, handsome fellow in his early forties, a typical North German. His father had been a university professor of a Lutheran Faculty of Divinity. He had been experimenting quite a lot and wrote a few papers on pain, using rather old-fashioned methods of approach. I got the impression that his activity in the Nazi's government administration had not permitted him to keep up with current ideas in Western neurophysiology, but we had some good discussions and were invited for supper to their house above Heidelberg. We also invited him once for luncheon at Schloss Hotel where he arrived in his motor car. When he had met us in the foyer he stretched out his right arm in the Nazi Salute, "Heil Hitler", which he did not do when we met him in his lab. But in the hotel there were people watching us and he wore the Swastika sign on his jacket showing that he was a member of the Party. Maybe that was the reason why the porter so generously lent me money each morning.

On the train from Würzburg to Heidelberg we had met a charming young lady, who sat opposite us in the compartment. She had a very beautiful head, her hair knotted in Grecian fashion, while in her fine oval face two big oval eyes smiled a little shyly at us. She turned out to be a native of Heidelberg, her father had an old-established decorating firm in the higher part of the

Fräulein Loni Hetzer, Heidelberg, at her weaving frame.

old city. There at the Kornmarkt she had her own shop where she sold home spun, dyed material and handwoven articles. She made things which Brita was most interested in. We spent a lot of time with Fräulein Loni Hetzer. One day she introduced us to her brother who was a young lawyer. He invited us on a tour up the Neckar Valley. He asked us to meet him some hundred yards below our hotel. We later learned this was because he did not want to appear there, as it was watched. He told us that he had defended

Loni Hetzer outside her shop in
Heidelberg, 1937.

a few politicians in the courts. He was thus in *Ungnade* and had
to be very careful.

We met them again after the war. The brother had refused to
become a reserve officer like most of his colleagues, and had served
as a private soldier in Russia. Before the Battle of Stalingrad he
had contracted typhoid fever and was sent back by air, which
no doubt saved his life. It was nice to see them again, people
whom we knew were already anti-Hitler before the war. The sister
came to Stockholm and stayed a few weeks with us.

We proceeded to Bonn where I was anxious to meet Professor
Uno Ebbecke, whom I knew in Stockholm in 1926. He and his
wife were also on board S.S *Minnekahda* in 1929. We made a
great mistake in calling on them at 2.30 p.m., which is visiting
time in Sweden. We woke them up in the middle of their siesta
and Frau Ebbecke, a gracefully tall lady, and an accomplished

94

painter, was rather put out when she came down to greet us. Uno Ebbecke was a very charming man, with many original ideas. He had a vast knowledge which extended over the entire field of human physiology. His studies of the peripheral circulation as well as his contribution to sensory physiology were well known, but of course he felt very deeply the isolation of the Nazi administration and World War II. We spent a few pleasant days making excursions to famous vineyards, and sampling their excellent Rhein wines. A steamer took us from Bonn to Mainz, from where we proceeded by train to Ostende, where we took a boat across the channel to England. Our tickets were only to Aachen, close to the Belgian border. I told the Belgian ticket collector this and asked him, in my school-boy French, to sell me a cheap ticket. He gave me a ticket for half the price, so I asked him to give me a ticket for Brita as well. He returned after a while and sold Brita a return ticket for a quarter of the price. When we were on board the Belgian Channel ferry I therefore asked for cheap tickets, but it did not work there. We were very happy to be outside Hitler's Germany, for although we had been very kindly and generously received we always had the unpleasant feeling of being watched.

In London we met our dear friends Arthur and Vera Hellström. They had a house in Redhill, south of London, with a beautiful garden where we spent a few days recovering from our long trip to Central Europe. I spent a day in Burlington House attending a discussion on nerve conduction at the Royal Society where I met a great number of young and old friends. A. V. Hill was in the chair, Alan Hodgkin, Alex von Muralt and many more read papers, and the discussion was very lively; Hodgkin's new ideas on the ionic theory of nerve conduction now being in *statu nascendi*. I remember sitting next to G. L. Brown and Alfred Sand; after the meeting A. V. Hill took a few of us back for supper at his Highgate house in the north of London. At the table A. V. Hill suddenly said, "Yngve, what do you think in Sweden about our armaments?" "Well," I said, "we do not think much of them. Go to Germany where every schoolboy receives military training and see how the Nazis have built up their Army, Navy and Air Force. If you do not introduce compulsory national service and take air raid precautions you'll meet a disaster within a few years." There followed a long silence. I felt a little embarrassed as A. V. Hill was not only a Secretary of the Royal Society but also a Member of Parliament for Cambridge and Oxford Universities. Three years later, in March 1940, one afternoon when I was writing a letter in my hotel room in Washington D.C. I heard a knock on my door and in walked A. V. Hill. "What are you doing here?" "I am here as an extra Air Force attaché to our Embassy." "Well, I am here as a kind of visitor, too," I admitted.

John Fulton had presented me a bottle of Canadian Club and thus fortified we had a very interesting talk for several hours. I asked him to forgive my outspokenness at his dinner party, which had produced such an awkward silence, "Don't apologise," said A. V., "we realized that you were right." "Well, you didn't need to have a prophetic mind to see that," I replied. "But why did you not do anything?" "What could we do?" asked A. V. "You could have raised the matter in the Royal Society, in order to tell the British Government what danger you were all in. In Sweden 500 Professors signed a demand to the Swedish Prime Minister to give more aid to the courageous Finns. It worked."

A few weeks afterwards I was invited for luncheon by the President of Columbia University. The other guests were Harold Urey , Nobel laureate for his discovery of heavy water, Professor Michael and Professor Selig Hecht. They were hungry for information about Europe in the awful days before the outbreak of the real war. I told them what I had seen in Germany in 1937 on my two visits, the second one with our Navy to Rostock. I also told them about A. V. Hill and that dinner party. "I am damned if you are not right," said Harold Urey, "we have to help Roosevelt;

there is no other way out." I do not know whether Urey, like other scientists, was at that time involved in atomic research or whether he was involved later; but I need not stress how important it was that the scientists joined up with Roosevelt at an early stage.

Let us now return to my hotel room in Washington in March 1940. A. V. Hill was most concerned about the very badly equipped British Navy, which lacked anti-aircraft guns even in its largest ships. From my shipmates in the Swedish Navy I had learned about this deplorable mistake on the part of the British Admiralty. Brita's brother was then serving in the Swedish anti-air artillery supplied by the famous new automatic Bofors guns which could be used to any elevation. As I said, A. V. was much concerned and told me, "Still worse is the fact that the Admiralty is making the same mistake as in World War I. They put their best and most intelligent young officers on board the battleships. They should be sent on antisubmarine defence, which will be far more important."

We were back in Stockholm by the beginning of June 1937. I went immediately on board H.M.S. *Svea*, the mother ship of a flotilla of three divisions of submarines. During that summer we paid a naval visit to Germany – but that is another story.

CHAPTER VIII

Naval visits to Estonia, 1935, to Norway and to Hitler's Germany, 1937.

Navies always pay each other courtesy visits. In 1931 I embarked in H.M.S. *Manligheten* at the Naval base of Karlskrona. At her mast flew the standard of its Commodore, Åkerberg, a small man, with a lively, cheerful temperament. I was to serve as medical officer on board the battleship, which carried four 10-inch guns and a few 6-inch guns on the sides; under his command and included in my medical care was a further division of three submarines and three destroyers. In the middle of June we steamed out of the port for a few days' naval manoeuvres in the water around Bornholm. The next morning the Commodore's aide-de-camp called on me. He felt ill and he looked ill, poor fellow. I made my examination. There was something wrong inside his abdomen, but I could not arrive at a definite diagnosis. It could be either the gall bladder or the appendix, but I could not decide which. I visited him in his cabin some hours later and found his temperature had risen and his pulse rate was relatively high. He looked in poor shape, so I went to the Commodore and told him that his adjutant was sick, possibly with appendicitis, and must be taken to a shore hospital. "Oh no," said the Commodore, "I can't lose him in the middle of the manoeuvres and, worse still," he added, "how will I manage in Germany without an adjutant?" "Well," I said, "I shall make a written statement that he is suffering from an acute abdominal condition, possibly appendicitis, and that I recommend he is immediately taken to a hospital ashore. If you do not send him, you must take the responsibility." The Commodore stood silent for a few seconds, looking earnestly at me, and finally said, "I suppose I shall have to take one of my destroyers off the exercise to take him to Karlskrona and the Naval Hospital." A few weeks afterwards, I learned that even the specialists were not able to make a precise diagnosis. The poor officer was sick, with a high fever, and had something wrong with the liver. He was, after some weeks, sent to specialists in Stockholm and was in bed for six weeks until he slowly recovered. I was very relieved that I had sent him ashore; meanwhile the Commodore had another lieutenant trained as his A.D.C.

On June 21st we steamed into the German naval port of Swinemünde where we spent four very happy days. On midsummer night (June 23rd) we invited the German naval officers with their wives for dinner in our wardroom. We had a very jolly evening. One of the commanders played the piano very well. He accompanied a pretty operatic actress, who sang for us. Suddenly the Commodore, who had had the German Commandant to dinner in his cabin, sent us a message that he would like to join us with his guests and offered us some bottles of champagne. We had no option but to invite them. When the champagne was served, the Commodore said to the commander at the piano, "Now Bäckström, you must give a speech telling our German friends that it is a special day of celebration in Sweden, Midsummer Eve." The commander rose and, leaning towards the pretty actress at the piano, said: "Meine verehrten Herrschaften. Heute Abend feiern wir Schweden eine besondere Hochzeit! Skål!" Broad smiles spread over the faces of our German guests, who were amused by his mistake of translating the Swedish, *Högtid,* which means holiday or feast day, into the similar sounding German word *Hochzeit,* which means wedding. One can understand the Germans' amusement.

One day a kind German engineer officer offered me a ride in a military motor car. He agreed to my request to visit the University of Greifswald where I called upon Professor Wilhelm Steinhausen in his Physiological Institute. The latter was very startled at my appearing in naval uniform, but received us very hospitably. We emptied a bottle of fine Rhein wine and he told me about and demonstrated to me his discovery of the mechanical mechanism and function of the labyrinthian ampullæ. It was interesting to visit this old university which was started by the Swedish King Gustaf II Adolf in the early 1630s.

In 1935 the submarine flotilla paid a visit to Tallin in Estonia, where we were warmly received by the Estonian officers, most of whom had served in the Russian Army before 1918. It was a fine old city with many memories from its Swedish past. I was even offered a plane to take me to Dorpat, where Gustaf II Adolf once founded a university. However, my flight was never made.

On the very first day our officers were invited to the casino on the beach of Pirita, east of Tallin, where we met a gathering of very nice officers and their wives, many of whom were very beautiful. I sat next to a fair-haired lady, the widow of an army captain who had once belonged to a Russian Guard Regiment. She was of old Baltic nobility. Her face, her singularly blue eyes and her corn-blonde hair reminded me very much of a Swedish classmate of mine, so I asked if she had Swedish ancestry. "Oh yes," she answered. "One of my ancestors was a Swedish officer who, in the middle of the eighteenth century, had to fly to Estonia where he took the name of Battenberg in order to deceive the Swedish agents." "How interesting," I said, and added, "His name was not by chance von Rosen." "How did you know?" asked my charming lady companion. "Well, your whole appearance and your complexion are so typical of the present family of von Rosen." She and her 12-year-old son took me for a walk afterwards to the ruins of Pirita, originally Birgitta (the Estonians, like the Finns, use P instead of B, Bank is Panku etc.).

The ruins were that of a Birgitta convent with a chapel that had once been an exact replica of the original convent of Saint Birgitta of Sweden in my birth place, Vadstena. It had therefore a special interest for me. When I entered the chapel I was astonished as

100

towards me came a huge white stork slowly lifting his long, red high-stepping stilts of legs. I took this as a good omen: on 27 December, 6 months later, the stork brought us another baby. It was our daughter Agneta, who arrived the day after Boxing Day.

The next morning, after a swimming session from the beach of Pirita, I invited the young widow, her son and five other friends of theirs for luncheon. I asked them to choose something they particularly liked. After a while the waiter entered with a huge soup tureen and served us with a Russian soup containing large pieces of beef, pork and vegetables which were ice cold – a very tasty meal in the hot weather. We had vodka and beer to accompany it. When I got the bill, it cost only 5 Swedish Crowns (one dollar!) for a meal for eight persons.

It was incredibly cheap to live in Estonia in those days. The country was rich in food, while the wages were extremely low. A university professor received a salary corresponding to $80 a month and he could comfortably feed a family on that. Only imported goods, like oranges, bananas, or clothes, were expensive.

Our sailors had a marvellous time, for they could afford to offer their pretty Estonian girl friends fine meals in good restaurants, drinking local liquors, snapps and sweet liqueurs. They took them in horse-driven cabs round the city and it was a comic sight to watch the sailors lazily stretched out in these droshkis, or hilariously landing on the quay in the half light of the early mornings.

We were royally entertained by our Estonian colleagues who took us to parties which did not end until early in the mornings. They had obviously preserved the old Russian habits. I found it rather funny to appear in full dress uniform at 2 a.m. at the Gloria Night Club and then to ascend the fall rope and salute the flag at 6 o'clock in the morning.

I also visited the market where they sold all kinds of fish, both fresh and smoked. The smoked eel and smoked whitefish are quite delicious and eaten a great deal in Finland and Estonia as an hors-d'oeuvre with snapps and beer. I could not resist buying 10 pounds of cloudberries, that delicious berry, rich in vitamin C, yellowish-red and as big as a raspberry, the fruit of a small herb which grows on the moors of North Sweden and also in Scotland. The cook made jam from them for me to give to Brita. It was most delicious with English pancakes for our Ostrogothian Thursday dinners, as a dessert after the yellow pea soup with pork.

I was standing on the bridge of the old pocket battleship H.M.S. *Svea* (the mother ship of submarines) in very stormy water steaming north over the Norwegian Sea towards Kristiansand when the torpedo master, an old petty officer, looking somewhat pale, came onto the bridge, stopped in front of the Commodore Blix, a son of the great Swedish physiologist, and reported: "Commodore, the torpedo heads are working loose in the store." What a frightening message! The heads contain all the explosive load of the torpedoes and apparently the torpedo master was very frightened. Commodore Blix, however, took it very calmly. "If the heads are loose you must take some men to help you to fix them again," he said without batting an eyelid. Just seconds later I happened to look up and discovered that the heavy top of the mast carrying antennas was working loose. "Look out", I cried, "the mast is coming down." "The doctor must go down below," said the Commodore, but I was only halfway down when the top fell with a frightful crash. Everybody had time to take cover, however, and nobody was hurt. Commodore Blix made no comment at the time but a few years later, when I needed a testimonial for promotion stating that I could endure sea conditions, he signed a statement for me.

We were not greatly pleased to learn that the naval squadron in which I served in the summer of 1937 was ordered to pay a visit to Germany. There were, however, a few submarine officers who looked forward to meeting their Nazi colleagues, as they had been

102

infected by the Nazi ideology. There were not many of them and they did not belong to those who were making a career of the Navy, just as in Germany, at that time, very few officers joined the Nazi party, apart from those who had failed to make a career of the services. But they were very noisy in the wardroom, cheering when they heard a speech of Hitler over the radio. The head of our division, Captain Hallström, was a very fine and wise man. At the official banquet in the Ritter Saal in Rostock the Gauleiter proposed a toast to the King of Sweden, expecting, of course, that our Captain would reply with a toast to Hitler, but he was cheated. Our Captain rose and proposed a toast to the German nation.

At the table I was seated next to a colonel who was chief of a Prussian infantry regiment, a highly cultured gentleman, who astonished me by his outspoken dislike of the Nazi régime. "They have sent that stupid Ribbentrop as Ambassador to London. He is making awful mistakes which will bring us to war with England again, just as in 1914." When we rose from the banqueting table, he said, "Hurry on ahead with me, so that we can have our own table without those black and brown fellows," indicating the Gauleiter's guards.

We were able to speak freely for an hour or two. He belonged to an old Prussian family, who had been officers for six generations, and he utterly disapproved of Hitler's military activities and particularly disliked his abandoning Christianity for a sort of home-made religion. This officer was certainly not an exception: it was a great pity and disastrous for Europe (and especially for the German people) that the old, well-trained and conservative school of German officers were not able to stop the rabid Hitler. There were quite a few attempts but they came to naught. The last attempt, which should have killed Hitler in 1944, organized by Starenberg, came too late. It might have been possible, in 1937, to change the fate of the German nation, but the leaders of other European nations do not appear to have been very wise either.

In the Physiology Labs at Rostock I met a young assistant, a Dr. P. His father was the Admiral's surgeon during the great Battle of Jutland in the World War I, the giant battle between the British and German navies. His maternal grandfather was the great physiologist, von Hering. Young Dr. P. had joined the Nazi party early on but realizing how it had developed he resigned – a very audacious action in those days. He was constantly under observation. I spent an evening in his apartment in Rostock. He told me some very interesting stories of the shocking state of affairs in Nazi Germany, while we emptied quite a few bottles of excellent Rhine wines. Coming out into the street at a late hour, I felt decidedly unsteady on my legs so, being in uniform, I considered it prudent to take a taxi, which took me all the way to my ship out at Warnemünde. The wines were certainly of finest quality as I woke up next morning without the slightest trace of a hangover.

CHAPTER IX

A great discovery and a charming man. — The international language of spikes.

In a series of beautiful experiments, using a method of cross-circulation between two dogs, Corneille Heymans of Ghent, Belgium, improved on his father's method and was able to demonstrate that a tiny little organ, the carotid body sitting like a wart on a small offshoot of an arterial branch of the carotid artery, close to its bifurcation under the mandible, exerted an important influence upon respiration. This little body, in man no bigger than the head of a match, has nerve fibres from the nerve of Hering, or the carotid nerve, a branch of the ninth brain nerve, the glossopharyngeal nerve, this also supplies the throat with sensory fibres and the back of the tongue with gustatory nerve fibres, running to the circumvallate taste buds on the posterior dorsum of the tongue. Heymans showed that lowering the oxygen content of the arterial blood flowing through the carotid body induced forced breathing in the animal and that, vice versa, an increase of the oxygen pressure of the perfusing blood caused a diminution of lung ventilation. Further, he was able to prove that the action of some drugs like lobeline, which were known to stimulate respiration, exerted their action entirely via the carotid body. In 1935 I had begun to investigate what kind of nerve fibres were mediating taste from the tongue. I was able to record responses from quite a few single fibres from the taste nerve, chorda tympani, which supplies the anterior three-fifths of the tongue with gustatory fibres. They were found to be A:delta fibres (about two to three thousandths of a millimetre in diameter). Now, turning to the glossopharyngeal nerve, I found its gustatory fibres to be of the same diameter giving spikes of only about one-fifth to a quarter of the spike height of the fibres responding to pressure on the tongue. As the carotid sinus nerve is a branch of the glosso-pharyngeal nerve, I subsequently looked for the fibres responsible for the respiratory reflex, expecting them to be tiny fibres of the same kind as the gustatory fibres. After all, their object was to signal chemical changes in the blood. This proved to be true: I could record the impulses as tiny spikes generally having a spike height which was only one-third to a quarter that of the largest fibres of the nerve fibres ending in the arterial walls of the carotid sinus and which responded to the stretching of the arterial walls in each pulse wave. These fibres served a vasomotor reflex exerting an inhibiting action on the heart and on the vasoconstrictor outflow to all the arteries in the body, relaxing their walls and thus lowering the arterial pressure. These large fibres had previously been studied by Bronk and Stella in the Johnson Foundation at Philadelphia. They had, however, hitherto overlooked the presence of the tiny spikes just lifting their peaks above the noise level.

I demonstrated my findings to our Physiological Society in Stockholm and wrote a short paper which I sent to Adrian in Cambridge, who was at that time one of the editors of the *Journal of Physiology*. After a few weeks, the manuscript was returned to me, Adrian writing to say that they had just received from Giulio Stella a paper with very much the same content. So I handed it to Professor Liljestrand, the editor of *Skandinavisches Archiv für Physiologie,* in which it was printed. About that time a third paper about these "chemoceptive fibres" from the carotid body was published by P. Rijlandt in Brussels. Thus we three physiologists, Stella in Padova, Rijlandt in Brussels and I in Stockholm were quite independently the first to record these chemoceptive impulses, thus giving direct proof of their existence. I am sure that this was quite decisive in Heymans's quite early award of the Nobel Prize in 1939.

Liljestrand was at that time doing experiments with Dr. Ulf

von Euler, who had spent many months in Heymans's laboratory in Ghent. I well recall that Liljestrand was rather inclined to doubt that respiration was influenced by the carotid body. He shared his doubts with many leading respiratory physiologists of that time. One of these, Dr Schmidt of Philadelphia, did not, as a matter of fact, give up his reluctance to accept Heymans's discovery until 1953, fourteen years after Heymans's award. Well, Liljestrand was no doubt convinced by my evidence. I am sure that Ulf von Euler contributed very much to his conversion and in a few weeks they found positive evidence, by recording the respiratory movement and the ventilation of the lungs. I would suggest that the coincidence of their findings and Heymans's Nobel Prize award was not quite accidental, as Liljestrand served as the powerful secretary of the Nobel Committee in Physiology or Medicine.

One day Ulf von Euler came to see me and said, "Why don't we co-operate? You have the set-up and experience in recording from the nerve, Liljestrand and I can contribute by making the blood gas analysis." It was a very good idea and we started in my underground premises to record responses of the carotid body nerve fibres to changes in the oxygen content of the arterial blood which flows through the carotid body. The nerve endings act as gustatory organs to taste the oxygen of the blood, signalling every slightest change in the oxygen supply of the organ. As Heymans had shown, these impulses impelled on the respiratory centre in the medulla, producing increased volleys of impulses to the respiratory muscles resulting in greater ventilation of the lungs and thus an increased uptake and transport of oxygen to the tissues.

I made the nerve preparations and the recordings from the nerve while Liljestrand and Ulf von Euler prepared the various oxygen mixtures which the animal breathed and Liljestrand ran backwards and forwards with the blood samples to analyse their oxygen content. We could therefore quantitatively compare the action and response from the nerve with the oxygen tension as well as with the CO_2-tension of the arterial blood. Thus we could demonstrate that these sensory organs of the carotid body were in action even in normal conditions, i.e. at the oxygen pressure of atmospheric air at sea level, and not only when the oxygen pressure falls to low values. Besides the sensitive respiratory centre in the medulla, we have thus another sensitivity centre for changes in the blood in the carotid body which is particularly sensitive to the oxygen tension of the blood, while the centrally situated respiratory centre is reacting on the carbon dioxide.

My old school mate Sven Jerring was working in the Swedish Radio, and through him I got to know their technical director, Johan von Utfall, an electronics expert, a most helpful, cheery gentleman. He helped me to make gramophone records of impulses in sensory cutaneous nerves in response to different stimulation of the skin; such records had been made in England by Adrian and Bryan Matthews from muscle spindles. One day Johan von Utfall came down with his recording bus to my underground room. There were no tape recorders in those days but quite broad and heavy steel bands which were magnetised. From these recordings gramophone records were made by the Swedish Radio. When at the end of October 1939, it was announced that Corneille Heymans had been selected for the Nobel Prize, I was asked to present his discovery over the Swedish Radio. World War II had just started and Heymans could not come to Stockholm. I wrote him a note telling him of the date and time for my broadcast and a week later I received a very charming letter from him, in which he told me that he had listened to the programme. "Je ne pouvais pas comprende la language Suedoise, mais la language d'impulse de nerf est une language internationelle." He had heard and understood the experiments played from my gramophone records. It is most fascinating how the development in electronics had enabled us to amplify these very feeble signals of our microscopic nerve fibres, enabling us to transmit them over the whole world. Heymans was very anxious to obtain my gramophone plates which, after the War, he used during his lecture tours in the U.S.A. He used them so much that finally, in 1965, I had to send him a fourth series of discs.

In 1947, on my way to the International Congress of Physiology at Oxford, I met on board M.S. *Britannia,* in the North Sea, Professor Alexander von Muralt; and as he wanted to listen to them, I put them on the gramophone in the smoking room. We were just listening to the effect of giving the cat 4% oxygen in nitrogen. The impulse traffic in the carotid chemo-receptive nerve fibres was sounding like the rattle of a Chicago elevated train when the Captain entered the saloon. He rushed over to the gramophone crying "Stop it, stop it. Something is wrong. I'll send the Sparky to repair it." It took us quite a while to convince him that there was nothing wrong with the pick-up on the gramophone. Converting nervous impulses into sound, however, does not produce beautiful music.

CHAPTER X

A wartime visit to U.S.A. in 1940 on a ship loaded with gold. — Sweden's aid to Finland in the "winter war" of 1939-40. — Physiology friends in America. — John Fulton and the function of the frontal lobes. — Lectures.

The Russian attack on Finland in November 1939 made an enormous impression on Sweden. Officers, doctors, nurses and people from all walks of life volunteered to got to the aid of Finland, whose army did so well during the first months of this unusually cold winter. Our Government, under the leadership of Mr. Per Albin Hansson, the leader of the Social Democratic party, was in a tight corner. Hitler's foreign minister, Ribbentrop, had made a pact with Stalin in 1939 giving the Bolsheviks a free hand in eastern Europe; Hitler had taken half of Poland and Estonia; the French and English had announced their readiness to send help to Finland, but via the Swedish Lapland railway. The Swedish Government could not accept this as it would have meant a breach of their neutrality policy, but the Swedish people wanted to help the Finns who were fighting so courageously. Aid societies were formed and millions of pounds were collected and sent to Finland. The university teachers sent in a petition signed by over 1000 asking for more aid to Finland. Gradually the Government gave in and sent a large number of Bofors anti-air-craft guns to Finland. My class-mate Rickard Åkerman, then an artillery colonel, went into the Finnish service.

In December 1939 I was approached by the Rector of the Karolinska Institute, Professor Gunnar Holmgren, while I was on leave from a mobilized submarine flotilla, to ask if I would go to the U.S.A. to encourage help for Finland. A Committee consisting of Holmgren and the former Swedish Consul General in New York, Olof Lamm, and some other people from the Foreign Office, were organizing a project to send out a number of Swedish scientists to the United States to tell the university people there of the urgent need for military help, particularly with aircraft and trained pilots for Finland. Count Folke Bernadotte had just been sent over in order to explore the situation and buy whatever was available – aircraft, guns, destroyers, etc.

As I had taken an active part with my friends Professor Theorell and E. Hammarsten in organizing Finnish aid, I gladly accepted. Life on the submarine mother ship lying icebound in the naval port south of Stockholm was tremendously boring. I had been called up on 1 September 1939 by a state telegram. It was a monotonous existence, and sometimes personally very embarrassing, because there were a few young submarine officers who were so taken in by the Nazi propaganda that in the wardroom they even stood at attention with their right arm out stretched in the Nazi salute when Hitler's voice was heard over the radio. They very cautiously avoided discussing anything with me, almost regarding me as a traitor because they knew my sympathies were on the side of the democratic Western countries. One evening, however, I had small revenge. Two of these lieutenants entered the wardroom and, hearing Hitler's voice, they stood at attention, right arms raised. But it was not a broadcast from Germany, it was a satirical impersonation over the B.B.C. coming from London; and it was a great pleasure to tell them this.

Just before Christmas I saw Mr. Lamm at his office; he was a powerful financier. I got very little guidance on what to do because the telephone rang almost continuously. He made quite a few deals ... a million here, a million there. Finally he said: "You see, I have to make a little money on the side," and wishing me good luck, dismissed me.

On the night of January 8th 1940, I kissed Brita and the

children goodbye and took the train to Trondheim in Norway, where I was supposed to embark on an American freighter, S.S. *Mormacport* of the Moore-McCormack Line, which was loading paper, etc., at the port of Langstein 18 miles east of Trondheim in the river part of the great fjord. Because of the bad weather, our departure was delayed a few days. Thus we spent two days in Trondheim where I visited the famous cathedral with Gunnar Westin, professor in religious history at Uᵣpsala University, a Baptist who belonged to our group. We were very cordially received by the Dean, Fjeldbue, who was to play a great role in the future in Norwegian resistance against the German occupation. I also met Dr. Ejnar Arnoltsen, medical health officer at the city of Skoensdal, not far from Hell, a small city. Once an Englishman who had visited Uppsala University had been so well dined and wined at Uppsala that he was more or less carried on to the night train to Trondheim. When he woke up in his sleeper late next morning, the train had stopped at a station. He drew back the curtain and read *Hell* on the station platform. He got such a fright that he jumped off the train on the wrong side, where on a magazine he read the sign *Godsexpedition*. Dr. Arnoltsen told me the mayor of Hell was at present on a lecture tour in the United States. An American impressario had arranged a six weeks tour for him in the States to talk about "Conditions in Hell". For this he was to receive 20,000 dollars, just the amount of money needed to build a new town hall in Hell.

Finally, on 13 January, we weighed anchor and went out into the stormy North Atlantic. The ship was well loaded with paper rolls for American newspaper and 100 million pounds worth of gold from the Bank of Sweden, so she moved rather ponderously in the sea. Professor Westin, who shared a cabin with me, was constantly seasick, poor fellow, and I gave him all sorts of pills, though they did not help much. But he was a brave man. He was a specialist on the history of the Baptist movement in the

112

U.S.A. and had crossed the Atlantic many times – and was always sick throughout the voyage. We passed south of Iceland; we could see the contours of their highest mountain Heklafjeld at a distance of 100 miles. That was on the only sunny day we had.

Early in the morning of 26 January, we arrived at New Jersey. The customs officials took my gramophone although it was made in U.S.A. (a Victrolia). I never saw that gramophone again, because it was stored somewhere. I was allowed to keep my collection of gramophone records, however, so I bought a fine portable electric record player in Sears and Roebucks for $25. But even that was taken by the customs in Genova in Italy in May 1940 – so I never saw that again either.

In New York I got a good room with a bath in Knickerbocker Hotel for $2.50 a day and rang up Dr. Watkins at the Swedish American Foundation. He came to my hotel and very kindly took me to the Swedish Restaurant "Stockholm". Suddenly during dinner someone shook my shoulder. I turned round and found it was Hans Lundberg, my old friend from Lidingö, who had become a pioneer in electrical, or magnetic, prospecting. When he was a young student at the Polytechnical Institute of Stockholm he and some classmates had discovered great copper locations in the north of Sweden. Hans Lundberg had gone to the U.S.A. and later to Canada and by 1940 he had a big company for prospecting in Toronto, Canada, and was very prosperous. He had married Signe Sjöberg, a most attractive brunette girl who lived near my mother's house in Lidingö.

Using magnetic electrical and gravitometric methods, he had mapped out enormous areas in Labrador and other parts of Canada. In 1959 he mapped out a great area of British Columbia for Axel Wenner-Gren, locations which now are just being exploited. His great contribution to technical prospecting won him the honorary degree of Doctor of Technology from his old alma mater, K.T.H. of Stockholm in 1958.

Professor John Fulton,
Yale University, 1940.

It was indeed a welcome reunion and Hans Lundberg took us over to his engineering club "John Ericsson", a clubhouse in English style, named after the great Swedish inventor John Ericsson, who invented the propeller for steamships, the fire engine, and many other important inventions. In America he is mainly known for his construction of the Monitor with its gun which destroyed Merrimak. There is a very fine statue of him in Battery Park at the most southern edge of Manhattan.

The following day I took the train to Newhaven to visit Dr. John Fulton, Professor of Physiology at Yale Medical School. I had written to him from Sweden, and he was very enthusiastic and active in supporting Finland. My headquarters in New Haven were at the Graduate Club at the Green. For the first few nights I was the guest of Lucia and John Fulton at their big house on Mill Rock at Hamden, a beautiful setting for a most charming and cultured couple. It was a wonderful place, with its large living

114

room filled with flowers, the great library with all its rare books, its dining room where their French cook, Marie, served the most delicious food – all in the finest taste, and redolent of the cordial atmosphere created by Lucia and John, who were both geniuses at friendship.

It was also most stimulating to accompany John to his laboratory in 333 Cedar Street. He was a pupil of Sir Charles Scott Sherrington, who shared the 1932 Nobel Prize with the present Lord Adrian for his great discovery of the integrative function of the nervous system, and had continued in his great master's footsteps. He was then working on the function of the frontal lobes of the cerebral hemispheres of anthropoid monkeys, which led to a series of very important discoveries. Among them was his observation that the ablation (cutting off) of the frontal lobes in a chimpanzee resulted in great change in the behaviour of the animal. Its aggressive behaviour disappeared completely; a former difficult beast was changed into a friendly, easily handled creature.

His reports were obviously not studied by any Swedish neurologist at the time but in Lisbon an old neurologist Professor Egaz Moniz read them and realized how to make use of this discovery.

One day an old psychiatric patient had entered his office, taken out a gun and fired two shots directly into his chest. Dr. Moniz would certainly have been killed if he had not the presence of mind to place both his hands on top of each other above his heart. The bullets went through his metacarpal bones and were stopped at the ribs, thus saving his life. But they destroyed his hands, so that he could no longer operate. However, when he read Fulton's report he at once got the idea of repeating Fulton's experiment on psychiatric patients. But instead of cutting away the frontal lobes, he developed a method of cutting the nervous connections between the cortex of the frontal lobes and the other parts of the brain within the white matter. So he instructed an assistant to drill a burr hole in the skull to introduce an instrument to

Egaz Moniz. The deformity to his hand caused by the bullet
wound can be seen.

cut through the white matter of the frontal lobes. The operation
was a great success. Agitated psychiatric cases who had to be
taken care of in mental hospitals were changed into friendly
tractable people who could return to their ordinary life. In 1949
Moniz received one half of the Nobel Prize for his discovery of
this "leucotomy" operation (or bilateral frontal lobotomy).
Although Moniz in the first reports on his operation quoted Fulton
and described how he derived the idea from reading Fulton's
papers, Fulton apparently was not considered for the Prize, which

116

was, of course, a great mistake. I suppose it was due to the fact that Moniz had been proposed but not Fulton, exactly as it was in 1923 when Banting and Macleod were proposed for the discovery of insulin, but not Charles Best.

Such mistakes could be made again. In order to prevent them I have for many years advocated a change in the statutes of the Nobel Foundation. As it now stands, nobody who has not been officially proposed by those invited to do so before 31 January each year can be put forward for consideration. Suppose, for example, that a referee who is studying the case of a candidate finds that another man should share the prize: even if his claim is superior to anybody else's, he cannot be considered for that year. My suggestion has been that in such a case the Nobel Committee should have a right to accept officially such a person as a proper candidate to share the prize with the scientist previously accepted as a candidate. I have tried in vain to introduce this change in the statutes, but the Supreme Court Judge, Per Santesson, who has worked out the new statutes which are now under consideration, considers such a clause adventurous as it might introduce possibilities of a coup. I know that his views are shared by many others – even by my friend Hugo Theorell (Nobel Prizewinner in 1955) who is much more experienced in this matter than I. He says that in such an event the matter can be taken up next year, when the Secretary of the Committee can ensure that the scientist in question is nominated in time. He means that it is very rare for a scientist to be given the prize the first time he is suggested, but I cannot resist adding that it has happened twice – with Best and Fulton – that a man who really deserved the award has missed it; and there is no guarantee that it will not happen again. But I have to admit that it could still happen even if my addition to the statutes were accepted.

In 1940 John Fulton was 42 years old and at the peak of his work. He had gathered around him a most impressive group of young expert physiologists: Barron, Thed. Ruch, McCulloch, Bob Livingstone, Nimes, David Nachmansohn and many others. With their help John Fulton entirely revised Howell's *Textbook of Physiology,* by then outdated. Thus the new era of neurophysiology was properly introduced. The book had enormous dissemination all over the world and its value in the promotion of this field of physiology cannot be over-rated, as it has been currently revised by Thed. Ruch and others.

All Fulton's young collaborators are now scattered over the United States – indeed the whole world – where they are in leading positions in research and teaching.

When only just approaching 60 John Fulton had to give up his brain research because of ill health. He devoted himself to his great hobby of medical history. He took on the job of organizing the Yale Medical Library to which Harvey Cushing, the great brain surgeon, Fulton's master in neurosurgery, had donated his collection. Despite his growing illness John Fulton wrote fine historical reviews and biographies and was always very cheerful even when his bodily strength was utterly depleted.

The last time I saw him, at luncheon at his house, he had his left foot bandaged. "It is just a classic textbook case of gangrene of the big toe," said John with a smile, lifting his dry Martini to a skål.

His years in Oxford with the great Sherrington and his years with Harvey Cushing, the most outstanding neuro-scientists of the first third of the twentieth century, had a great influence on the young Fulton who certainly possessed the ability to absorb all there was to take, and to use it in his own research and pass it on to others. But above all, those of us who knew John Fulton will remember him as a most lovable man. He certainly possessed the gift of friendship.

According to the brief diary which I kept during my trip to the U.S.A. in 1940, I lectured in the morning of 30 January to Fulton's class of students – on "Escape from sunken submarines", which included a good deal of respiratory physiology. In the afternoon I gave a lecture on the function of the carotid body. The Chairman was old Professor Yandell Henderson, a great authority on respiratory physiology. At the end of my lecture I let the audience listen to the rising noise of nerve impulses from the carotid nerve when the animal was given air low in oxygen. My experiments were recorded on gramophone discs by the Swedish Radio in my laboratory. After I had played these discs, Yandell Henderson rose and said: "I did not believe in this chemoceptive business but now I have to surrender. There cannot be any doubt that the carotid body has an important influence upon respiration."

We had received Mr. and Mrs. Yandell Henderson for dinner in our apartment in Stockholm in 1935 when they returned from the International Physiology Congress in Russia. He then told us how pleased he had been to find the first part of his name Jundell in the Stockholm telephone book. Henderson was of Scottish origin and now he had discovered that he was also of Swedish origin. A slight smile spread over the face of Professor Johansson who had been a class mate of old Professor Jundell, whose father Jundelski, came from Poland. His son had taken the *ski* off the end of his surname. Fine old gentleman that Jöns Johansson was, he just smiled. None of us wanted to deprive our old friend Yandell Henderson of his happy illusion.

The next day, 31 January 1940, I was met at Washington airport by Gösta Håkansson from Orlunda near Vadstena, my birth place. He had in 1908 passed his exam at the teachers' Seminary at Linköping. He then emigrated to the United States and started medical studies in Chicago. He had previously qualified in Swedish massage and earned his living by giving massage. During World War I he had joined the U.S. Navy and had now advanced to the rank of Captain in the Medical Corps and was the administrative director of the Navy's great Research Center at Bethesda.

He drove me to the Swedish Legation where I delivered the courier mail I had brought from the Swedish Foreign Office in Stockholm. There were no Atlantic flights in those days. Gösta Håkansson insisted that I stay in his apartment. He was just divorced: his only daughter was in college and he led a bachelor's life in Washington. He took me to lunch at a club, where we had cocktails with some young ladies. One was Miss Newton, stepdaughter to Admiral Ross, President Roosevelt's surgeon, and the other Miss David, who was a niece of Admiral McIntire, the previous Surgeon Admiral of the U.S. Navy. I met both these surgeons later in the evening and it was a very valuable introduction for me, because, thanks to them, I was received later on at the submarine base at New London and by Dr. Zworykin, the inventor of the television camera. (I do not remember which of these two young ladies Gösta married soon afterwards. He was, however, or perhaps I should say he happened to be, at Pearl Harbour on the Sunday 1942 when the Japanese bombed and destroyed the whole Pacific flotilla.)

In 1940 Gösta Håkansson was a very handsome fellow in his early fifties. He played the piano well and he also sang. We had corresponded for a few years before my visit. When we met now, after 30 years, he was very disappointed to find me and not my tall, handsome brother Agne (born in 1889) who had been his friend at Linköping. He had not heard of my brother's death in 1913. Furthermore, he was very annoyed by my propaganda on behalf of Finland. "It has taken me twelve years to feel myself an American and I do not want to feel like a Swede again," he said. He was certainly right. It had taken him many hard years to reach a relatively high position. Now a frequent guest at the White House, he belonged at the top of the Roosevelt administration. He had to be American, not Swedish, and he had also acquired that special relaxed manner which is characteristic of a real Yankee. This did not fit in very well with my then rather hypomanic ways.

120

He warned me several times saying that I would wear myself to death. I listened, of course, to his kind advice, but how could I act on it in those days?

The following day I had luncheon at the Roosevelt Hotel with Admiral Wijkmark and Prince Bertil and Commander Hård af Segerstad and a few others in the Swedish Naval Commission sent out by our Government to buy everything available for our Navy. They nearly succeeded in buying a big American destroyer. Prince Bertil (who was a Naval Officer and a specialist on fast motor torpedo boats) spoke very good English. We had met before in the Swedish Navy and we share some very highly appreciated reminiscences of a "Lövmarknad", a fair on June 22nd at Karlskrona, a naval port in the southern Baltic. The Prince is an excellent speaker and a great help to his father King Gustav Adolf. As a young man he was a very good athlete and a great authority on motors; he is popular in widely differing circles.

One day I paid a visit to the Diving Unit Naval Yard of Washington where I met Captain Behnke and Captain Willman. They were doing some very interesting research with helium gas for deep water diving. It was a most interesting visit and I was very grateful for all this valuable information both now and later. I met Behnke later in Heidelberg after the war, in Stockholm and in San Francisco. He has made many important contributions to deep sea diving.

On February 3rd 1940 I was invited to a meeting in Dr. Gunnar Myrdal's apartment, 448 Riverside Drive. There I met Professors Nordenson, and Westin, Birger Nordholm, my old classmate from the Grammar School, the Swedish Consul General Kastengren, Mr. Tore Munthe and Dr. Richard Sterner. The latter was Myrdal's assistant in his work on the Negro Population Investigation which they performed for the Carnegie Foundation. A few months later Gunnar and Mrs. Myrdal returned to Sweden on a freighter of the Tordén Line to Petsamo in North Finland. At the end of the war

Gunnar Myrdal entered the Swedish Government as Minister of Commerce, taking Dr. Sterner as his State Secretary.

Gunnar Myrdal was, of course, as usual bursting with ideas; while Alva Myrdal, whom I had met and worked with before, was more practical. They were a most charming couple, full of wit and brilliant ideas, and highly cultured. They have an enormous influence on Swedish social thinking, not to speak of Gunnar Myrdal's contribution to International Economy. His *An American Dilemma* was a best seller in the United States, and a year ago his great work *An Asian Drama* was published, the result of many years' study of Asian sociology and economics while his wife Alva was our ambassador to India in New Delhi.

Gunnar Myrdal is a very good speaker and always improvises his speeches. A political opponent, Professor Georg Andrén, a former conservative member of our Government, once said: "When Gunnar Myrdal steps up on the platform in the Chamber (of our Riksdag) he looks very sad because he does not know what he is going to say. When he leaves the platform he looks very happy because he has already forgotten what he said."

A few days later I took the train to New London where I met the officer in command of the submarine base, Captain Robert Edwards, and met Dr. J. H. Shilling who was the medical officer responsible for developing the "free ascent" with "lungs" from a sunken submarine. For this purpose they built a 100-foot high tower. At the bottom was a replica of a submarine compartment from which you escaped the 100 feet up to the surface of the water tower. Such a tower was copied for the Swedish Navy and everybody serving in submarines trained to make escapes in these towers. A few sailors and a demonstrator are locked in the compartment, and water is let in until the pressure is equal with the water pressure outside in the 100 foot tower. Then the "lungs", respiratory apparatus like those which skin divers use, are adopted and every man in turn escapes to the surface. They have been instructed previously on how to use their "lungs" and it has been emphasized that, while ascending, they have to let out the compressed air in their lungs continuously. It they close their glottis the air expands the lung, which is very dangerous. Dr. Shilling gave me all the details of this, for which I was most grateful. He had had a few accidents as we have had in Sweden. Shortly before my visit an instructor who had made many hundred "free ascents" suddenly came up unconscious and died, for no obvious reason. Dr. Shilling was very upset, but in spite of all possible precautions such accidents happen in diving. It is a profession with its special dangers and even skin diving is a dangerous sport if you do not observe the precautions strictly.

I had a very good discussion on these matters with Dr. Shilling, who later in April took me as a guest to their home for a few days. The Shillings and their children were very musical and one of the children, although only 11 years old, was a gifted pianist. Captain Robert S. Edwards even invited me to go on board their salvage ship *Falcon*, a ship which played an essential part in the retrieval of quite a few of the crew from the sunken U.S. submarine *Squalus* for which they used their new method of deep water diving, exchanging the atmospheric air for a mixture of helium and oxygen.

The chief purpose for my tour to America was, however, to visit the universities all round the States and tell them what Sweden had done for Finland, thus stimulating and creating a climate for more aid to Finland. John Fulton helped me very generously by writing to his friends all over the States. Thus, I received invitations to lecture at many universities and after my lecture at Yale University, I proceeded to Harvard University. The night before Dr. Norton Canfield, professor of otology, had given me supper in New Haven and he gave me so many highballs later in the evening that I woke up with a frightful hangover. Fortunately, Dr. McCulloch drove me up to Cambridge, Massachusetts in his sports car which took four or five hours, by which time I had recovered and was able to deliver my lecture on the chemoceptor drive on respiration. Professor B. W. Cannon had generously put an hour of his own lecture schedule at my disposal at 4.30 p.m., so I had the large auditorium in the big white marble building of Harvard Medical School.

There on the front benches sat a long row of famous European physiologists, refugees from Hitler's and Franco's regimes, like von Brücke from Innsbruck, Pi Suñer from Barcelona and many others. There were more than 200 people in the audience and I ended up by playing my recordings. Dr. Alexander Forbes was also present, then aged about 60; he had worked with Adrian in Cambridge. He became very enthusiastic when I told him about Professor Holmgren's project of trying to find volunteer pilots for Finland and about my plans to send Swedish students to the U.S.A. to train as pilots. He had an airplane himself and told me about the plans of the Civil Aeronautic Authority in Washington D.C. which supervised a wide project giving university students preliminary pilot training all over the States. (He was going to visit the Civil Aeronautical Authority in Washington D.C. and raise the subject of training Swedish students in aviation.) I was invited to stay overnight with Dr. Hallowell Davis, but Alex Forbes took me back with him to his home. Before going to bed we went to a skating rink in the vicinity.

The next day I went to the editors of *Christian Science Monitor,* a fine paper known all over the world for its reliability and sound judgement in international affairs. They listened very intently to what I told them about Sweden's aid to the brave Finns. I had to answer a good many questions and they very generously offered support. They also retained a very friendly attitude towards Finland and Sweden all through the war.

In the afternoon Dr. McCulloch drove me to Worcester in Massachusetts where I stayed with my friends, Dr. and Mrs. Hudson Hoagland at Clark University. Hudson had spent a winter in Cambridge working with Adrian, and Bryan and Rachel Matthews had taken them up to Swedish Lapland during Easter of 1931 where they lived for a week in an igloo. They returned via Stockholm where we had an opportunity to entertain them. They were all very delightful people and fine scientists.

I gave one lecture in the afternoon about carotid chemoceptors. Then I played ping-pong on the veranda with a very pretty young lady. She was very good at it and I lost heavily as I could not return her services. Finally I said: "You screw too much." Hoagland's young assistants who had been watching our game suddenly disappeared and my opponent, very red in the face, said: "For Heaven's sake don't use that word. I *spin* the ball."

After dinner I gave a lecture on "Touch, Pain and Tickle" to a rather large audience.

The next morning Hudson Hoagland wanted me to prepare and isolate the sinus carotid nerve in a cat, which I did. I had done it many hundreds of times in previous years but not for more than eight months, but it succeeded and Hoagland and his students could listen to the noise of the nerve impulses from the nerve. You could hear the baroceptive impulses from the carotid wall exploding in a volley for each heart beat. It sounded like an old steam engine puffing up a hill.

Then Hudson Hoagland gave a very fine talk on his research on the perception of time. He had been able to prove that the reaction time varies with the body temperature according to Arrhenius's law about the relation between temperatures and the velocity of chemical reactions. After lunch I took the train to Meriden north of New Haven where Dr. C. S. Schneider drove me in his car to the Wesleyan University in Middletown. There I gave a lecture and demonstration to their Biological Society and they were all very generous and interesting people to meet. I returned late that night to the Graduates Club at Yale.

There the next morning I phoned Consul Lindholm in New York,

125

wrote letters to Count Folke Bernadotte and to our Swedish Minister, Boström in Washington telling them about Alex Forbes's support, etc., and gave Minister Boström all the details I had obtained about the aviation training of students, class plans, etc.

Two days later I went to Chicago on a non-stop flight in the evening, in a DC 3. It was the first time I ever flew after dark, looking down on large cities lit up at night and I was much impressed. My old friend and colleague, Dr. Ralph Gerard, met me at the airport and we had a long talk together that night at his home and with Margaret, his colleague and charming wife, who was a pupil of Ranson the great American neuro-anatomist. That evening I had a long talk over the phone with Count Folke Bernadotte, who was staying with his in-laws the Manvilles at White Plains. He reacted positively to my plans and wished me further success and I later sent him the full programme from the Civil Aeronautic Authority. The next morning I visited Ralph's lab. and paid a long visit to Dr. Kleitmann, the great expert on the physiology of sleep.

CHAPTER XI

Visiting St. Louis, Los Angeles and San Francisco. — An aerial trip to Seattle.

Professor Joseph Erlanger had sent me an invitation to St. Louis and he met me at the airport and drove me directly to his house where he gave a great dinner party for the whole medical faculty of the Washington University including the president of the university. They were all very eager to learn about conditions in Europe, which was still in the "phoney war" stage – no shooting or killing – Hitler was limbering up, the whole of Europe was jittery, but in America life went on as ususal. After the dessert Joe Erlanger asked me to give a brief survey of the actual situation in North Europe which I did for about 20 minutes and then we had a long, friendly discussion. I happened to tell them that I had met Gunnar Myrdal working on the negro population problem so Erlanger said: "What advice does Myrdal give?" "Oh," I said, "he believes in the education of the coloured people." "Just that," said Erlanger, "education and intermarriage." There followed a long silence at the table interrupted only by a few significant coughs. You must bear in mind this happened in 1940 in Missouri.

I spent another night with the Erlangers and Mrs. Erlanger, who had been a school teacher, was a most charming, witty hostess, full of anecdotes, while old Joe Erlanger made the very best "Old Fashioneds". He had two tall and beautiful daughters whom I had photographed at Harvard in 1929, and I met one of them on this occasion.

Erlanger understood the implications of my research and I was exceedingly grateful for his generous support. He and Gasser had discovered that there were sensory non-myelinated fibres; I was the first to connect them with delayed pain and also the first to record impulses from single fibres of this kind. I owe much to both Erlanger and Gasser for their generous understanding of my little handicraft with nerves at a time when I was considered rather useless by the Swedish authorities. Erlanger's generosity extended beyond understanding: he made the university give me a honorarium of $250 which enabled me to pay a visit to California.

I spent some very exciting days there. Dr. Alrick Hertzman took me to his physiological laboratory at St. Louis University where I talked to 150 students about carotid chemoceptors. I met Dr. Doisy the biochemist who had just synthetized vitamin K, for which he was awarded the Nobel Prize in 1952. I had long talks with Erlanger, Blair, Rioch and Jacobson in their labs. and it was all very useful to me. In the evenings I dined at the house of the young assistants, and danced with their pretty wives at Chase and other restaurants. I had a really good time, forgetting for a few days the threatening situation in Europe. Years later, when after the war I dined with the Coris at the Theorell's house in Stockholm, the night before they received their Nobel prize in 1947 Gertie Cori said: "So you are really a professor of physiology; I thought you were a *professeur de danse!*" They were a most delightful couple who had grown up in Prague. Gertie Cori was already by that time looking rather pale. She developed pernicious anæmia, which she fought very bravely for many years but to which she finally succumbed in the middle of their important research.

Both Alrick and Gertrud Herzman were of Swedish descent and both visited us in Stockholm later. Although born in the States, Gertrud spoke an idiomatic Swedish; her parents always spoke Swedish at home. Alrick was doing fine research on the circulation in the skin, basic work which was to prove very useful later on in the preparation of special conditions for the American astronauts. One day when I visited the large Museum with portraits by the great Swedish painter Anders Zorn (including a portrait of the brewer family Busch), Hasselberg's fine sculpture the "Frog" and Mille's "Folke Filbyter", I met Dr. Martin Nilsson the *rector magnificus* of Lund's University in Sweden (one of his sons became also rector). He asked for news from Sweden, told me that he was the guest of the President of the University and was very magnificent indeed, as in those days professors at our ancient provincial universities often rather aspired to be when they had to meet such an inferior person as a young lecturer from another university!

On 16 February, Gertrud Hertzman served us a delicious luncheon at their house and Alrick drove me to the station for a train to Kansas City where I boarded the train "The Chief" on the Santa Fé railroad to Los Angeles. It was my first acquaintance with the very luxurious American cross-continental trains. There was a fine dining car, a saloon car where you were served with any drink you wanted and at the end of the train an observation car where you could enjoy the awe-inspiring scenery of Colorado and Arizona.

On the train I met a very handsome, middle-aged and well-dressed gentleman, Mr. Gildchrist from Winnipeg. He was a most interesting and entertaining fellow. He was the son-in-law of Searle of Searle & Company, who was one of the greatest wheat kings in the world. The company had sent chemists to Uppsala to study cereal protein chemistry in Professor The Svedberg's laboratory. Mr. Gildchrist told me about his world-wide business transactions. He had met Mussolini several times, doing business directly with the dictator. I remember that he said: "Watch out, Mussolini is failing. Previously his mistress was an intelligent, talented Jewish woman who helped him with his business transactions and they made a good team. Now he has deserted her on Hitler's orders and taken two young girls who will kill him." In fact, they did not; in 1944 Mussolini was shot and although Clara Petucci threw

The author picks his first orange in California, 1940.

herself in front of him to protect him, the machine gun bullets killed them both.

In Los Angeles I was very cordially received by the head medical officer, Dr. Sven Lookrantz, in his beautiful home. He had been chief physician for the Olympic Games in Los Angeles in 1932. He was in a very poor state of health, as his heart was failing and he was confined to an armchair. Nevertheless, he was most helpful, ringing up the Biltmore Hotel to make a room reservation and telling the manager that he was not to charge me more than $2 a day for a room (with a bath). "How can you do it?" I asked. "Oh well, you see its my duty to inspect the hygiene of the hotels, so what the hell." With him was a young friend, Friberger from Stockholm, who was told to take me to dinner in a Spanish restaurant in the city, where we were served a most delicious Mexican meal and entertained by some of the waitresses who were not only very pretty but also good dancers, and the guitarists were excellent. The restaurant staff, all Spanish speaking, knew Dr. Lookrantz very well. His very attractive wife belonged to a family of early Spanish settlers in California.

California seemed like paradise to me. I saw oranges growing for the first time and picked them from the tree; I swam in the Pacific; on 20 February it was 16°C in the water; and I visited the famous places where film stars thronged at night. Dr. Wiersma demonstrated his famous experiments on crab nerves which have been so fundamental for basic neurobiology; I met Mrs. Strömberg, the wife of a well-known Swedish astronomer of Mount Palomar Observatory. In 1915 she had been a nurse in my mother's nursing home. She gave me the latest edition of her volume of poetry and even played the piano for me: she was an excellent musician.

The following day I met Berndt Balken, the famous Norwegian-born American aviator, who listened to my plans and advised me to write for appointments with Mr. T. Lee of the Boeing School, Oakland, and Eric Nelson the aviator, who had been born in Stockholm and who was the first man to fly round the world. He gave me his address in Seattle. The next day all the papers reviewed King Gustaf of Sweden's speech. The Government had forced him to tell the world that Sweden was a neutral country and could not extend more help to the valiant Finns who now were beginning to fail in the face of superior Russian forces. It was, of course, politically expedient to say this, but it saddened our hearts. I spent a few hours discussing the situation with the very kind Swedish Consul, Walter Danielsson. Everywhere you saw headlines, "Sweden will not help Finland".

In that afternoon my friend Jack Schultz, who had worked a few years in Stockholm with Brita's cousin, Professor Torbjörn Casperson, drove me to my first lecture on the carotid nerve at the California Institute of Technology at Pasadena. Then Professor and Mrs. C. A. G. Wiersma gave me an excellent meal and at 7.30 I delivered my second lecture that day on "Touch, Pain and Tickle". There was a very long and lively discussion afterwards. I remember particularly the great interest which Dr. Lorente de No from the Rockefeller Institute showed and Prof. Henry Borsook who was doing research on *tic doloreux*.

On the "Daylight" train to San Francisco I met an old and fascinating Hawaiian lady who had been lady-in-waiting to the Hawaiian princess. She told me about the visit of Crown Prince Gustaf Adolf and his wife Louise on their journey round the world in 1926 and how much "my Princess enjoyed the visit of this highly cultured Royal pair". I had a room in the Saint Francis Hotel on the eighteenth floor. When that building was new in the spring of 1906, my father-in-law woke up there because his bed had slid from one wall to the other: it was the great earthquake.

On the very first night I met Sven Söderblom, the youngest son of our famous Archbishop. He was a clerk in the shipping department of Panama and Pacific, and told me many interesting things, among them the fact that the Douglas Company sent a lot of important equipment to Vladivostok. I found that interesting as Mrs. Douglas, a few days earlier, had given $100.000 to Finnish aid.

That is what is called "Business as usual". Do not let the left hand know what the right hand is doing! All this time American scrap iron was being shipped to Japan to build up their navy to fight the Americans.

Although the situation at the frontier in the south of Finland, where the Russians had concentrated enormous troops looked very grave, I pursued my aim to get help to the Finns.

I also met and was generously received by our Consul, General C. E. Wallerstedt, to whom I gave all the details of my scheme and who also reported to Boström in Washington, and I received a very encouraging telegram from Folke Bernadotte asking me to continue and wishing me luck.

I gave a few lectures at Berkeley, where I met their great anatomist H. M. Evans, who I knew from his visit to Stockholm in 1927 when I was a senior medical student. (I took him for supper at Zorn's restaurant, "The Golden Peace" in the old city of Stockholm and we became very good friends. I was not to know at that time that he would become such a great man. He should have

132

shared the Nobel Prize with Dr. Houssay from Buenos Aires for his discoveries about the growth hormone – the third mistake which has been made in that award.)

After my last lecture Dr. Helen Starbuck, a bright girl working in neurology, drove me over the beautiful bridge to San Francisco where we had an enjoyable supper at Saint Francis Hotel. She had spent some time fairly recently in Cambridge, England, and I was very interested to learn about my friends and colleagues at the Cambridge Physiology Lab.

The next day I visited Mr. T. Lee, G. Meyers and Mr. Daniel at the Boeing School which was equipped with all the most modern instruments. I had the pleasure of flying in a Link Trainer for aviators. Then I flew to Seattle where Eric Nelson met me at the airport and drove me to his beautiful house by the shores of a lake outside the city. Eric Nelson was born in the south of Stockholm but went very early in his life to America to make his career as a pilot. In 1930 he flew round the world and became attached to the U.S. Air Force. At the time of my visit he was one of the directors of the Boeing Company. He was a tall, handsome fellow, then about 50 years old. In the living room he had a big intarsia picturing Stockholm city and the river, a very beautifully fashioned piece of art by an old friend Jerk Werkmäster, a schoolmate of Brita at Rättvik in Dalecarlia.

Eric Nelson took me out for supper to a very fine large restaurant. The head waiter was an old Stockholmer, Harald Hellström. As Washington State was dry we were not served any drinks or wines, but after the meal we were invited to the office of the French chef in the middle of the large kitchen, where we were served fine French cognac with our coffee. We then went around and were admitted to a few private clubs where liquor flowed copiously – there was hardly a sober person there.

The following morning, after being served breakfast by Nelson's Japanese butler, we had a long discussion about my plans. We got hold of a stenographer who took down and typed for me Nelson's very valuable advice. I had four copies made, of which I sent two to Folke Bernadotte. In the afternoon we met Nelson's friend Toby Hill, a very nice young man who arranged an interview for me with his paper the *Seattle Examiner,* the largest morning paper, which was owned by Hearst.

Early next morning I went by DC 3 to San Francisco. We ran into bad weather – a very strong head wind. The pilot was forced up as high as 13,000 feet. As the cabins in those aircraft were not pressurized, the air stewardess had to put on her oxygen mask and I saw that the colour of my finger nails became rather cyanotic. We should have landed at Portland and at Sacramento, but could not come down at either of these airports. Finally, when after seven hours' flight we were over the San Francisco district, the pilot announced: "Because of bad weather and fog I have to circle. If I do not find an opening within ten minutes we have to go for Salt Lake City." But after about five minutes he landed us at San Francisco's small airport. When I got out of the plane I said to the pilot, "What a pity you did not take us to Salt Lake City, I have never been there." "Oh," replied the pilot, "we should never have reached it. I hadn't enough fuel for half that distance."

At Stanford University I visited Dr. James Murray Luck, the editor of the *Annual Reviews of Biochemistry* as well as of *Physiology.* I had been asked to write the review "Sensory Organs" for the 1941 issue. As I was rather heavily engaged I suggested, and it was agreed, that Ragnar Granit should write about vision, Ernst Bárány about hearing and I about the cutaneous senses. Murray Luck introduced me to Dr. O. L. Webster, professor of physics, who was a very keen aviator, having his own plane, a small Cubman. He got very enthusiastic about my scheme to train Scandinavian students in the U.S.A. He took me up in his small plane several times and let me take over the controls. I loved it, as I managed to land the plane quite well on several occasions. Mr.

134

Webster took me to the President of Stanford University, Dr. Ray Lyman Wilbur, who was once President Hoover's Minister of the Interior. He was a very tall man, impressive in appearance. He listened for a long while to my plans and offered his help. He promised that the University would receive 200 Scandinavian students in the student dormitories for training at Stanford Airport. During the following few days a full scheme was worked out. In San Francisco I discussed my project with Axel Axelsson Johnson, the son of the owner of the great Swedish shipping line Nordstjernan which sent ships from Sweden to the Pacific Coast through the Panama Canal. He suggested that his father's ships could bring the students to San Francisco for their training. The whole project got fairly detailed planning. The economics were particularly good as everybody was very keen to help the Scandinavians, apart from a few communist students at Stanford who learnt about our plans and fiercely rejected the idea of helping Finland against Russia, as they wrote in their own paper.

I was therefore very encouraged and sent long telegrams to Minister Boström in Washington D.C. and to Professor Gunnar Holmgren in Stockholm, being very anxious to get their agreement; and I waited for a week in San Francisco but received no answer. The situation at the Finnish-Russian frontier in the South became very grave.

All that time I was in touch with our Consul General in San Francisco, E. C. Wallerstedt, who was most helpful. He invited me for luncheon with his Vice-consul, K. O. von Essen, and a young attaché, Hichens Bergström, at the Stock Exchange where I admired the wonderful alfresco painting by the famous Mexican artist Ribera. I was also invited to a ceremony in Wheeler's Hall in Berkeley, where Wallerstedt handed over the large gold medal, the diploma, and the cheque to David Lawrence who had not been able to go to Stockholm in December 1939 to receive the 1939 Nobel Prize in physics because of the war. I dressed in tails, white tie and top hat, as we do in Stockholm for those ceremonies, and found I was the only one who had done so.

Afterwards I met David Lawrence and his brother, Dr. John Lawrence, and I was invited to see his new big cyclotron in Berkeley. Both brothers Lawrence were very charming men, full of life and spirit. It was a great loss that David Lawrence should die so young. Somebody told me that there were too many surgeons involved in the operation from which he died at the age of only 44.

While waiting for news from Sweden and our legation in Washington D.C. I visited laboratories and people. At Stanford Graduate Club I had luncheon with twenty leading scientists who asked me to give a talk about the situation in Scandinavia and about the Nobel Foundation, etc. I met old Colonel Söderblom, the elder brother of our previous Archbishop. He had been active in the Spanish-American war and still wore a Napoleon. We had yellow pea soup and pancakes in the Swedish Club (on a Thursday of course) and the club members there collected money for Finland Relief. Thus I got to know quite a few of the Swedish colony in the Bay District: Sven Söderblom, Ernst Seebohm, Thurston, Axel Axelsson Johnson and many others. Day after day I waited for instructions from Sweden. Meanwhile the situation grew graver in Finland. Finally on March 8th 1940 I had to leave California to attend the meeting of the Federation of American Biologists at New Orleans. So I invited my young friends, Dr. John Lawrence with his girl friend Catherine Douglas, Richard and Ingrid Hichens Bergström, James and Janette Murray Luck and Helen Starbuck to a Swedish supper at Saint Francis's Hotel. I had bought provisions at a Swedish grocery and obtained Swedish *anjovis* and pickled herrings, so we had a kind of Swedish *Smörgåsbord*. The French chef made some very delicious small sandwiches, each with a stick decorated with beautifully cut paper in the Swedish colours – blue and yellow. He even made a very fine *Jansson's Temptation* from my instructions – a dish of chopped raw potatoes, anchovies, onions and full cream baked in the oven. It was a great success eaten with Swedish aquavit O. *P. Andersson.* The very gay company made me forget my disappointment for a while. We danced and had a really good time until rather late.

Early next morning I met James and Janette Murray Luck on the "Daylight" train to Los Angeles, where Janette's sister and parents joined us for a very merry supper at Bona Gusta, a Spanish restaurant, and just before midnight James and I boarded the night train for El Paso. The following day we met Dr. Douglas Smith, the famous protein chemist a Berkeley, and young Mrs. Bess Christian Carson Febiger Spahr of the famous Febiger publishing family of Philadelphia. We played cards together and had a lot of fun for two days until we reached New Orleans.

There I finally received a telegram from Minister Boström, who asked me to visit him in Washington D.C. and from Alex Forbes who had paid a visit to our legation. So I see that I made an entry in my brief diary:

"The project seems to be progressing."

CHAPTER XII

Meetings at New Orleans. — Adventures in Washington
D.C. An angry ambassador. — A famous inventor. — A
celebrated sculptor. — Denmark and Norway are occupied
by the Nazis.

New Orleans in the middle of March was just lovely. The azaleas
were in bloom everywhere. It was fine weather, perhaps a little
more humid than I was used to but otherwise very comfortable.
I went at once to a shop for men's wear and bought myself a thin
suit. It was my first pair of trousers with a zip. My friends joked
about it saying that I now stood a great chance of being circumcised,
if this had not been done before.

I met John Fulton and most of my physiology friends. After
the meetings John always gave a large cocktail party in his suite
at the Roosevelt Hotel. There I met two very skilled women
doctors, Dr. Grace Goldsmith from Tulane University and Dr.
Grace Roth from the Mayo Clinic. John and I took them to a late
dinner at Arnouds, the Creolan Restaurant, where we had large
oysters and their speciality, Creole Chicken. There was also a young
girl called Shirley Carter Cordill who worked the electrocardio-
graph in Tulane's Medical Clinic. She belonged to an old French
family. On our last night in New Orleans she invited me for dinner
at her parent's house in Walnut Street. Her father was an old
banker who was very worried about the Long administration in
the State of Louisiana. It was Huey Long II who succeeded his
brother Huey P. Long when he was shot a few months earlier.

I met a Tulane medico who told me the full story about Long's
assassination. Huey Long was an extremely active fellow and a great
admirer of beautiful women. Many of them fell for the great Governor, the author of the book *Every Man a King*. He was very

attracted to one young lady who, however, resisted him, which made him more anxious than ever to conquer her. When he did not succeed he tried to avenge himself by starting a rumour that the young lady had a touch of negro blood – a rather bad thing to say in the South.

One morning when Governor Huey Long climbed the stairs to the entrance of the Capitoleum in Baton Rouge, the girl's boy friend, a young medical man, stood there on the terrace. Huey recognized him and asked: "Oh, are you here to see me?" The answer was three bullets which killed him instantaneously. The young boy friend was immediately shot down by Long's bodyguards.

At the time of my visit, in March 1940, the Governor was busy building a huge monument to his brother before his period of office expired.

Old Mr. Cordill became very heated and called them robbers, etc., but after a while he and his wife calmed down. Their coloured servants served us a most excellent dinner. Their house was full of beautiful antique French furniture and paintings by old and modern French painters; their garden was full of exquisite trees and bushes in blossom, gardenias, camelias, etc. I sat there in the lovely warm Southern night hardly believing that it was real and completely forgetting that I had that morning received a telegram from my friend Hugo Theorell which started: "Idiot, you must complain to the King." It had taken him some time on the telephone to pursuade the telegraphist in Stockholm to accept the message. I was supposed to send in my appeal against the decision of the Uppsala Medical Faculty which put my competitor first for the chair in physiology, in spite of the fact that three out of the four referees had placed me first. But all that belongs to another chapter.

In New Orleans I met Herbert Gasser and had long talks with him on the sensory function of the tiniest non-medullated nerve fibres to the skin. It was an important subject for me, and I felt exceedingly pleased listening to his comments. Next year he brought up the whole business again when he wrote a fine review on pain which I had every reason to be grateful for. Five years later, I would have the great pleasure of welcoming him and Joe Erlanger to Stockholm when they received their Nobel prizes.

Dr. Grace Goldsmith had earlier been assistant to Dr. Hilding Berglund, my brother Agne's classmate in the Medical School in Stockholm. Berglund, after his first wife's death in the "Spanish Flu" epidemic in 1919, had emigrated to the U.S.A., where he first spent some years in Dr. Otto Folin's lab. in Harvard before becoming Professor of internal medicine in St. Paul, Minnesota. Grace Goldsmith was a very ambitious young doctor with a wide knowledge of nutrition. She has made fine contributions to this field and early on in her academic life became a full professor at Tulane University Medical School where she still is head of a Clinic. I saw her in the 1950s when I went down to New Orleans. She received our daughter Helena at Christmas, 1951, and took her to the Sugar Ball where she became a kind of queen, with her portrait in the *New Orleans Piccanyer*. Grace Goldsmith also visited us in Stockholm during the summer of 1954 when something very dramatic happened. I had brought Grace back to Stockholm from our cottage in the Archipelago and Dr. Carl G. Schmiterlöw and I were just entertaining her in our house in Experimentalfältet when Brita rang me up from the island. "I have been stung by a wasp," she said, "and have a rash all over and my tongue is swelling." Her voice became more and more slurred. I was greatly alarmed, and ordered an ambulance plane to fly over, knowing that it was just these first 30 minutes which were critical, and would decide whether she would survive or not, so they too knew pretty well how dangerous it was.

It took me 1½ hours to reach our cottage and there I found Brita out of danger. She had already recovered. I gave her a antihistamine pill, that was all, and in the evening we went to a crayfish supper together. So I missed my supper with Grace on her last night at Stockholm, but Carl G. Schmiterlöw was my stand-in, and gave her an excellent supper at Operakällaren.

But Brita never goes out anywhere in the summer without taking with her some antihistamine tablets in case she is stung again by a wasp. Now, since it happened to me too, I take with me cortisone tablets as well.

On the Sunday (March 17th, 1940) Grace Goldsmith drove me north, out in the country, so I saw part of Mississippi, and the following day I took a small plane and flew to Baton Rouge to have a look at the new State University which Huey Long had built there. He also built a new Community Hospital close to Tulane Hospital. That was his revenge against the Tulane University, for not giving him an honorary degree, or so I was told. The university at Baton Rouge was a very costly building, a enormous Colliseum, a copy of the ancient one in Rome. I much enjoyed the pilot letting me take over the controls of the plane. It took us one hour to fly, but nearly 4 hours to come back to New Orleans by bus.

We took off in an Eastern airliner (a DC 3) at noon the next day and were due to land at 7 p.m. in Washington where Captain Håkansson was to meet me at the airport. But I did not, in fact, arrive by air, because there was a steady head wind and at 6.30 the pilot announced that he could not land at Washington because of bad weather. So he landed twelve very angry passengers at Richmond at 9 o'clock. We had to take taxis from Richmond to Washington, arriving about midnight. I rang Gösta Håkansson's bell and he came down and let me in.

"What a pity," he said, "I was expecting you at the airport at 7, but the plane at 7.45 landed and you were'nt on board. I was going to take you to the White House with me, for supper." You can understand now why I am not very well disposed to Eastern Airlines, and always try to avoid using them. Perhaps I am being unfair, and I ought to be grateful to them for their caution, as conditions may have been so bad that landing with a full load of passengers could have caused a disaster.

Next day Minister Boström took me to luncheon at the Mayflower Hotel. He had received all my reports and they were all neatly stacked on his desk. When I asked him what he had done about them, he answered: "I am waiting for instructions from Sweden." He got very red in the face when I was bold enough to ask him why had he not taken any initiative. In fact he became so purple that I was frightened that he was going to have an apoplectic fit. But he calmed down, drank a glass of wine at one gulp, and after a while said: "I gather that you have been very energetic, young man."

In the afternoon Alex Forbes visited the Swedish Legation and had a long talk with Boström and his chargé d'affaires, Wennerberg. Forbes told them that the Civil Aeronautic Authority would give all the help it could to train Scandinavian students to fly, but there was little enthusiasm on the part of our diplomats. That night I went to dinner with the young secretary Åke Sjölin, who told me that the situation in Europe was getting very serious. Nobody knew where Hitler would strike the next blow – it could be Scandinavia.

I busied myself by visiting Food and Drug, where I saw Dr. Durrett who helped me with the registration of "Pancreotest", a Swedish product originally produced by professor Einar Hammarsten and Dr. Gunnar Ågren, and now produced by the Swedish Pharmaceutical Company, Astra. I also saw a good deal of Alexander Forbes who took me one afternoon to the Spanish Embassy where he was staying. His brother Malcolm, a former Governor of the Philippines, had been Roosevelt's emissary to Franco's government in Spain. The Spanish ambassador, de Cardenas, and his wife, who was Romanian and very beautiful, were a charming couple, and received me warmly, though I am sure they breathed a sigh of relief when I left. I was so ill-advised as to tell them that I had

142

met quite a few Spanish scientists in exile in New Orleans, and that these men wanted to go back to Spain. "They are thieves and murderers, who have stolen the gold which belongs to the Spanish Bank," cried de Cardenas, in a towering rage. His wife tried to calm him, but it only made things worse when I told him that my friends in exile were all good Spanish patriots and that a country like Spain could not afford to lose so many of its best scientists. "You must take them back," I continued. "Why can't you do what they did in Finland, where they reached some kind of reconciliation after the civil war of 1918?" Hjalmar Procopé, the Finnish minister to Washington, had just entered, "Ask Procopé," I said, "he will tell you how they have succeeded in Finland. Do you imagine that they could have put up such a brave fight against the Russians if there had not been a social reconciliation in the country?"

Hjalmar Procopé was not, however, anxious to be involved in our dispute. Everybody was congratulating him on his approaching marriage to a beautiful Irish girl.

Alex Forbes had invited me to fly in his private plane to New York, but the weather forecast was too bad for him to attempt the flight, so be borrowed 20 dollars from me and we flew to New York where I went to see Dr. Selig and Celia Hecht in their Columbia University apartment in Claremont Avenue. I walked right into a children's party given for their daughter Marezza, which was most amusing. The next day I had a talk with Berndt Balken the aviator, and Captain Cornelius, later going on by rail to New Haven to spend an evening with Norton Canfield and John Fulton. I returned to New York the next day just in time to get a ticket for the first night of *Liliom*, Ingrid Bergman's first appearance on the stage in America. I tried in vain to buy some flowers, and in the end sent in a box of after-dinner mints packed to look like a doctor's prescription.

Alva and Gunnar Myrdal, 1940.

Rec/ One tablet after each exit from the
stage. *Repetite sine scrupolo.*

Yngve Zotterman

A few days later I received a note from her via the Myrdals,
"The chocolates apparently stopped me feeling nervous and were
very good; I thank you cordially for your kind letter, Ingrid
Bergman."

I got a seat in a box and just below discovered Alva and
Gunnar Myrdal, Eva Nyblom, editor of the Swedish Magazine *Idun,*
and Elsa Brändström Uhlig, "The Angel of Siberia" as the German
prisoners of war in World War I called her. She and her husband
were now in America, in exile from Hitler's Germany.

For various reasons I was very anxious to visit Dr. Vladimir
Zworykin, the inventor, known all over the world for his invention
of the *ikonoscope,* the first electronic television camera. I have
heard that Zworykin went to L. M. Ericson Company in Stockholm
in about 1927 with the idea of making a photo cell mosaic of the
same general dimensions as the mosaic of photoreceptors (cones and

144

rods) in the retina of our eyes. But the L. M. Ericson people were not interested, so Zworykin took the idea to R.C.A. in the United States. In 1929 he took out a patent and a year later it was manufactured. He had also invented the electron multiplicator and built one of the very first electron microscopes.

I was specially interested in obtaining thermionic valves with the lowest possible internal noise for my own work and had previously written to Zworykin about this. I now took the opportunity of visiting him at the R.C.A. research laboratories at Camden. I had telephoned to say I was coming, but when I arrived was not allowed in until they had phoned the Navy Department in Washington where, thanks to Gösta Håkansson, I was satisfactorily identified. Dr. Zworykin took me round the labs and showed me his new electronic microscope, and we had a long discussion about using his electron multiplicator for low noise amplification.

Finally I said: "Dr. Zworykin, have you built any television cameras with infrared sensitive cells." He looked at me over the top of his spectacles for a few seconds and then looked at his watch and said: "I am very sorry, but I must leave you now, as I have an important engagement." So I left his lab. As I emerged into the forecourt of the building, I met my friend Selig Hecht, Professor of Biophysics at Columbia University. "What the hell are you doing here Yngve?" he asked. "I could say the same to you," I retaliated. "I am here to ask Zworykin to make me a gadget so I can study the behaviour of insects in the dark," was his reply. It was therefore understandable that Zworykin had not answered my question, as it touched on "classified" work for giving the Navy instruments to enable them to navigate in misty or foggy weather.

Returning to Washington, I spent some time discussing the situation with the young Swedish attaché, Åke Sjölin, and the commercial councillor Erickson, and I also visited Captain Behnke again in the Navy Yard. I spent one night in the house of the Finnish legation secretary Salanko, and met some very interesting

145

soldiers like Captain Merton and General Janinen from Finland, who had devised a machine gun. They were all very worried, as the military situation in Finland grew steadily worse.

After two days in New York I was invited to the Hechts for a dinner-dance in the Columbia University Faculty Club. I then flew to Cleveland where I attended the annual meeting of the American College of Physicians. There I met my old friend Norman Wetzel, with whom I worked in 1926 in Sir Thomas Lewis's lab. in London. One day he took me to see Carl Wiggers, a distinguished expert on the physiology of circulation. I had always appreciated his excellent textbook of physiology, so it was a pleasure to meet this great teacher. I also saw Dr. Grace Goldsmith again; she was examined and made a fellow of the College of Physicians at this very meeting.

In my hotel I struck up an acquaintance with a Swedish American, Wretman, who used to lunch there every day with a special group of businessmen and politicians. One of them was Harry E. Payer, formerly Assistant Secretary of State in Washington. They were very kind to me and invited me to lunch with them several times. Later, however, I was warned by some American colleagues that this group of men were conducting rather dangerous business, and were involved in all kinds of racketeering. One of them had bought up and completely ruined an old-established company or so I was told.

There was a large stamp exhibition at the hotel attended by stamp collectors from all over America, among them a Swedish American, Mr. Lagerlöf of New York. He took me round the exhibition hall, and on every stand he was greeted with: "Mr. Lagerlöf . . . how do you do." Perhaps you would be interested in looking at my little collection, etc." He stopped at a few stands and bought stamps, some of them for rather large sums. I believe he bought about 20,000 dollars worth on that morning alone. When I told him of the reason for my being in the U.S.A. he became very interested and promised me that he would donate five small Piper Cubs or the equivalent to Swedish universities, to help train the students. A few weeks later he sent me an invitation card to a parade in New York where he was an honorary colonel of a New York regiment, but unfortunately I was unable to attend. Mr. Lagerlöf gave the Swedish Postal Museum seven fine collections of stamps, among them, for example, the two Mauritius stamps of 1847. They are worth at least $100.000 today, and the other stamps colleetively are worth the same.

On 4 April 1940 I flew to Detroit where I was met by Dr. Gesell, professor of Physiology, at Ann Arbor. He and his daughter, and his colleagues Dr. Bean and Dr. Winder, took me to dinner at the Swedish Restaurant "Stockholm" in Jefferson Avenue. This big restaurant on three floors, a former American millionaire's home, was managed by my old playmate from Vadstena, John Sjunnesson, and his very capable wife Siggan, an experienced restaurant manager. It was a Thursday, so we were served the Ostrogothian yellow pea soup with pork, with which we had hot Swedish punch and then, as a dessert, English pancakes with strawberry jam.

In the evening we drove by car to Ann Arbor where I was installed in a room in the Union Club. My room had been shut up for some time with the central heating full on, and the temperature was up in the nineties. I opened the windows, turned off the heating and sitting in a robe at the writing desk occupied myself by writing reports to Sweden until 4.30 a.m. by which time the temperature had dropped enough for me to sleep. The following morning at 9 I gave a double lecture to Gesell's class. Whether it was my over-heated brain or Gesell's having had too much of the Swedish punch the night before, I do not know, but my gramophone blew up when they connected it to the d.c. mains and their projector could not take my English sized lantern slides. So I had to talk for 2 hours without my recordings or slides; all I had was the blackboard.

In the afternoon Dr. Edgar Kahn, a brain surgeon, was kind enough to take me in his private aircraft to Detroit where I stayed with Siggan and John Sjunnesson on the top floor of their house in Jefferson Avenue. There I received an invitation by Dr. McClure, head surgeon of Ford Hospital, to spend a day looking round this fine hospital where they had done some excellent research on new methods of treating burns. One of his surgeons, Dr. Heading, had spent some time with Professor G. Nyström at Uppsala.

The following day a young man drove me to the Ford factories, where I saw how the cars were manufactured from the foundry to the panel pressing and conveyor belts. It was a very impressive sight. Because of the heat in the foundry, they had introduced the use of salt tablets to avoid heat strokes and fits. Those men working there sweat more than a gallon a day, and lose a good deal of mineral salts. They must therefore drink a lot and also replace the minerals lost, otherwise they receive alarm signals from the central nervous system.

The so-called "miner's fit" which often afflicted miners in the very deep, hot coal mines in Wales was caused by a deficiency in mineral salts, which was demonstrated by Dr. Jack Haldane in England. The miners sweated up to two gallons a day and compensated for their water loss by drinking the water in the mines, which is totally free of salt. By adding a certain amount of salt to the drinking water the "miner's fit" became a thing of the past. When living in a hot climate, where you sweat a great deal, it is important to have a sufficient amount of salt intake besides the water one drinks.

In the evenings I used to dine in Sjunnesson's elegant restaurant "Stockholm" which was patronized by a lot of important and well-known people. One day I was given lunch there by the Swedish Club and their Travellers Club. The Chairman was Helmer Åkerman, who was a member of Otto Nordensköld's Expedition to Tierra del Fuego in 1900. When they went ashore a huge group of naked natives advanced to meet them and the situation looked rather grave. Then Åkerman, raising his gun said; "If you, Professor, take the King, I'll take the Prime Minister." Otto Nordensköld could not help bursting into a shout of laughter. The natives stopped, quite nonplussed, and after a while the explorers were able to negotiate with them.

By some means Dr. McClure had engineered me an invitation to luncheon with Henry Ford. So I was driven out to the restaurant at Fords where I met an elderly man who had been the Wright Brothers' mechanic. He entertained a young woman journalist (Miss Dorothy Scriven of the London *Daily Telegraph*) and me with stories of the first American aircraft and the first parachute jumps made by the Wright Brothers in the early years of the century. After a while a secretary came in and said: "Mr. Ford is sorry, but a committee from Washington has just arrived so he cannot see you today."

When my guide Richard Crosse from the Ford Public Relations Office, asked me what I would like to do, I said, "Please drive me out to see Carl Milles, the famous Swedish sculptor who lives and works out at Cranbrook." Miss Scriven asked if she could join me and an hour later I knocked on the door of Carl Milles. An elderly Swedish maid opened it and took my card and we were led into the studio, where he received us most warmly. In one corner of the studio stood his statue of de Geer, the famous nineteenth century Swedish industrialist; in another corner was a new group of sculpture for the Rockefeller Center (a horse rider, a nymph and a faun) and on his easel the huge head of a Red Indian in Mexican onyx.

Milles was in very good spirits; he told us a lot of stories of his early life and about friends like Romain Rolland and others who went to Switzerland during World War I as they wanted to keep out of the politically overheated atmosphere. We talked about his

Carl Milles in Cranbrook, Ohio, 1940.

house on Lidingö, built during the general strike in 1909, where I used to climb up the rocks when a small schoolboy.

We were asked to stay for tea and he showed us the great park around his and the architect Saarinen's house, where we saw full-size copies in bronze of many of his famous sculptures like Europa and the Bull.

We also saw his collection of antique Greek and Roman sculptures, mostly torsos and fragments but still very beautiful. "How were you able to get these beautiful things out of Italy?" – "Well," he replied, "One has friends".

He certainly has. Every visitor to Stockholm knows that he must visit "Milles's Garden" – "a beautiful outdoor museum with all his sculptures on the terraces high up on the rocks of Lidingö", facing the busy port of Stockholm. There he spent his last 10 years, always working hard, as geniuses do. Even his genial storyteller's art has been preserved for the future as two of his broadcasts over the Swedish Radio have been recorded on tape.

150

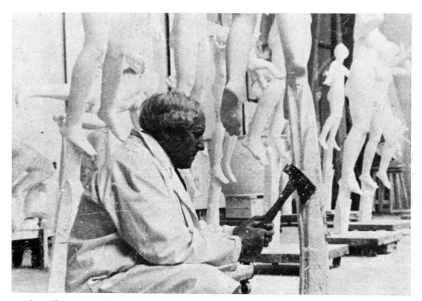

Carl Milles in his studio at Cranbrook, Ohio, 1940, working, on his fountain for the cemetery in Washington.

That evening while having supper in Sjunnesson's restaurant, we heard very alarming reports over the radio. Nazi troops were attacking Denmark and Norway. We heard the excited American radio reporter describing German troops marching through Karl Johan's Gate in the main street of Oslo. The King and the Government had left Oslo.

The next day I telephoned the Swedish legation in Washington to ask for news. I was told that Sweden had not been invaded by the Nazis, so I could proceed according to plan to Toronto. Canada was of course involved in the war. So on 12 April I flew to Buffalo, where we landed in a very heavy snow storm, and took the train to Toronto where I was met at the station by Sten Lundberg, the younger son of Hans and Signe Lundberg. He drove me to Hart House, the comfortable university clubhouse, a fine building in Gothic style, like the colleges in Oxford and Cambridge. I paid a short visit to Charles and Margaret Best and had supper at the Lundberg's house with the Swedish Consul Ander and Mr. Janes, manager of the Canadian SKF Company and his wife. We listened repeatedly to the alarming radio reports of Nazi occupation of Norway and Denmark. There was no news from Sweden.

When I returned to Hart House about midnight, the Warden, Mr. J. B. Bickersteath, invited me into his living room. He had been sent to Canada by his friend Baldwin, the British Prime Minister. He was a very interesting fellow, at least 110% British! He instructed me in the art of breakfast in hall. I had to take a morning paper and eat my breakfast in silence as all conversation in the morning was strictly taboo. Bickersteath told me how he had belonged to the "Cliveden set" who in the earlier 1930s had flirted with the Nazi regime, believing that it would help to combat communism. He had visited Germany and attended the Nazi festivals at Nuremberg where he had got to know Göring, Hess, Göbbels and other high Nazi leaders. Now he was very disillusioned. He was apparently anxious to know more of me because every night, regardless of the very late hours I kept, he was waiting to call me in for a chat by his fireside.

One day I was invited to lunch by Dr. Cody, the president of the University, who asked me to give about an hour's review of the situation in Scandinavia to a group of twelve professors including the Dean Dr. Grant and Dr. FitzGerald, Professor Edgar McLeod and Professor Frazer.

Charles and Margaret Best entertained me very well. I visited the insulin factory and Banting's and Best's laboratories, and found them very well-equipped organizations. I had tea in his laboratory with Frederick Banting, who was in uniform. He shared my anxiety about the grave situation in Northern Europe. He was well aware that England was insufficiently armed against Hitler's forces. We had a long, absorbing talk. A few months later he was killed in an air accident.

During the next few days in Toronto I was constantly in touch with the Swedish Consul Ander who was very kind and helpful. There was still no news from Sweden and I was rather bewildered as I did not know how I could get back there. The last Swedish liner had left in March.

I returned to New York, stopping a few hours to see the Niagara Falls where I met the Swedish manager of the big electrochemical soda factory, Mr. A. Heilborn. After I had seen over his factory he took me to lunch and then drove me to Buffalo where I got a plane to New York. That evening was spent in the Myrdal's apartment in Riverside Drive. Gunnar and Alva Myrdal had gathered together several Swedish people, Dr. Richard Sterner, Mr. Naboth Hedin, head of the Swedish American News Office, B. Svensson, New York correspondent to the morning paper Stockholmstidningen, Birger Nordholm, head of the Swedish State Travel Bureau and Eva Nyblom, editor of *Idun*.

Gunnar Myrdal was, as we all were, very worried about the situation in Sweden and the lack of news, and we talked for hours. I remember I said that there was not much we could do now except await further instructions from the Swedish Government. "You are a clear defeatist," said Gunnar Myrdal. "We must start work straight away. If the Swedish Government capitulates to Hitler, we must set up an exile Government over here like the Danes have."

Although I was not fond of the Swedish Government and particularly not of Mr. Bagge, the head of the Educational Department who appointed university professors, I could not fall in with Myrdal's idea. I telegraphed home and received a cable from the head of the Medical Naval Corps, Dr. Herbert Westermark: "Go home via Italy and Germany."

So I went to the German and Italian Consulate in New York, got the necessary visas and then booked on S.S. *Conte di Savoia*. She was to sail on 27 April.

Before sailing I spent a few days in New Haven with Professor Burt Andersson, the dean of the Yale Dental School and his wife, Florence, whose mother with her sisters were singers who had toured America in the 1890s. They had been very successful and the great Bohemian composer Smetana had written many songs for them. Florence sang these songs and I accompanied her on the piano, following the original handwritten scores.

On April 25th I gave my last lecture in Schermer Hall of Columbia University where I had a large audience of about 200 people. Selig Hecht was the chairman and we had a fine discussion afterwards. There were Harry Grundfest and George Wald and many others. Professor and Mrs. Michael gave us dinner in their house and afterwards we went to a reception and dance given by the President of Columbia University.

It was indeed a brilliant party, the gentlemen in tails and the ladies wearing very elegant dresses and jewellery. I danced a lot with Celia Hecht and Florence Michael, who was a very good dancer – she still is. She told me that she never gave up going to dancing lessons. The next day I made a phone call to the Consul General in Stockholm and received $300 for covering my travelling expenses to Stockholm. My last day in New York I spent at the Rockefeller Institute where I had lunch with Dr. Landsteiner, Dr. Grundfest and my Finnish colleague Dr. Therman and had a farewell dinner with my very helpful friend Dr. John Watkin of the Swedish American Foundation at the restaurant Stockholm. I was now feeling rather worn out; the future looked obscure and uncertain.

I had been offered posts in St. Louis and at Columbia University if I preferred to stay in the United States until war was over. These were very generous offers by my friends, but I had my family in Stockholm. I had to be with them and I had to obey the orders of our Navy Medical Department.

CHAPTER XIII

Return to war-stricken Europe. — A world-famous run-ner. — A great politician. — Berlin during the "phoney war".

On the morning that I sailed for Europe, Eva Nyblom came to my hotel and gave me a pink carnation and a letter to her friend Mr. Höckerberg, a prominent publisher in Stockholm (a year later they were married). She also helped me to buy a few things for Brita, like seamless silk stockings.

I had a big cabin with three beds all to myself. There were very few passengers, as nobody went to Europe in those days unless they had to. We were served lunch and I went to my cabin to sleep for a few hours before dinner. I had very congenial neighbours at my table including two ladies. One was Mrs. Gallo, wife of the owner of the Carlos Grand Opera Company, on permanent tour in the U.S.A., a gifted soprano who sang under the name of Sophie Charle-bois. She was a most cultured lady who knew many Swedish opera singers, like Jussi Björling and Joseph Hislop. She amused us by recounting stories about the adventurous life of a touring opera com-pany. The other was a Mrs. Olga Klein who came from Belgrade. She and her husband, both Jewish, had left Serbia for the United States, her husband being frightened in case Hitler invaded Serbia. She was now eight months pregnant and a most attractive lady with rich auburn hair. We had very stormy weather at first and she did not appear for some days, so I paid a visit to her cabin. She was so seasick that she was afraid she might give birth prema-turely. I listened to the foetal heart beat and finding everything satisfactory I gave her some anti-seasickness pills that I had – "Vasano" I believe – and she improved. She told me that she had left her husband in New York. He did not dare to go back to Serbia, so she had left him as she so much wanted her baby to be born there. "I will fight the Nazis," she said. She was very beautiful and had apparently been much courted. She showed me a scar on the back and front of her left chest from a bullet which had penetrated her lung and just missed her heart by a few millimetres, and was fired by a jealous Serbian officer who had shot her when she gave him the cold shoulder.

I have often thought of her since and wondered what happened to her when the Nazis overran her country. When I visited Belgrade in 1965 I asked about her but nobody knew anything. I wonder whether she escaped or whether she and her baby were both killed. I very much admired this courageous, beautiful lady, a great Serbian patriot, who preferred serving her threatened country to a safe, peaceful life of luxury in the United States.

A famous passenger was of course Paavo Nurmi, the great Finnish runner, world champion in 1500–10,000 meters track running, and several times an Olympic gold medalist. He had toured the United States on propaganda work for his country. To say that he did not talk much is an exaggeration – he never talked at all. But he took to me, as he understood Swedish fairly well. On one of the first evenings on board, I gave him a drink at the bar before dinner, and then he offered me a drink and so on. Before the third drink I took an olive. Unfortunately that plump olive had a stone and I broke one of my front teeth. As there was no dentist on board I tried to fix the parts together with various kinds of adhesive, but with very little luck.

On several evenings I played bridge with the two ladies I have told you of and André Phillip. He was a Professor in national economics at the University of Lyon and also a member of the deputy chamber of the French Parliament. He was a tall, handsome, enormously active man who, when not playing table tennis with me, walked rapidly along the lengths of the decks reading a book – *Utile Dulci*. He told me that when he was 18 he made up his mind that he would be a university professor before he was 30, a member of the chambre des députés before 40 and a member of the French Government before 50. With a satisfied smile he said that he became a professor at the age of 26, was elected to parliament when he was 36, and had expectations of joining the Government before he was 50. As a matter of fact, he joined de Gaulle's exiled government in 1942 and served as Ministre de Finance in the French Government from 1946 to 1947.

When we arrived at Gibraltar we were inspected by the British authorities, much to the annoyance of the Italian officers. Phillip was anxious to leave the ship at Gibraltar but the British would not allow him to do so. Then he telephoned the French Government and the Foreign Office managed, through their colleagues in London, to arrange for him to disembark at Gibraltar, so he left our ship and flew to Tangier. From there he went on by air and reached Paris on the night of 5 May 1940.

Another passenger was a Belgian, who had served as commissionaire for the Belgian Pavilion at the World Exhibition in the United States. He told me how happy he was that the Belgian King had made a treaty of non-aggression with Hitler, so that Belgium would be saved from war this time. Poor fellow, he reached Brussels on the night of 9 May 1940, the very night that German troops began to invade Belgium and Holland.

Anchored in the Straits of Gibraltar was a great fleet of merchant ships waiting to be escorted out into the Atlantic. One of the finest of them, at least in appearance, was the Swedish M.S. *Brageland*. There were also two Norwegian tankers and a Danish East India Liner. The whole fleet of forty-two ships weighed anchor at 2 p.m., and what an impressive sight it was to see them steaming out.

We journeyed through the beautiful sunny Mediterranean but we were uneasy because we all felt that something terrible was going to happen soon. We had excellent food and the crew had plenty of time to look after and entertain the handful of passengers. They also printed a ship's paper, in which I read that Selma Lagerlöf, the famous Swedish authoress and Nobel laureate of 1909, had died a few days earlier. The paper contained a four-column obituary of this great little lady, whose novels have been translated into Italian and forty-five other languages. On 6th May we passed through the Gulf of Naples and I saw the beautiful island of Capri (where I have written most of this autobiography) for the first time. We landed beneath the old Castello and the red Royal Palace. We had six hours in Naples so I had time to visit the famous Marine Biology station where I met Dr. Dohrn, the director. He was very worried, for although of German descent he feared that Italy would be drawn into the war on the wrong side.

We left Naples at 6 p.m. and landed at Genova the next morning. The Italian Customs even confiscated my new American gramophone which they packed and sent to Stockholm. I had to pay 69 lire for the freight, and never saw it again. I sent a telegram to Brita and had a nice lunch with wild strawberries as dessert; later I was taken to a very good restaurant by the secretary of the Swedish Consulate, Mr. Odner. I met a young man, Åke Samuelsson, who worked for a travel bureau and accompanied me all the way to Berlin. We could not get a sleeper, so we spent the night sitting up. In Milan a German journalist entered our compartment. He was very pleased to get news from the U.S.A. and was particularly pleased when I introduced him to Paavo Nurmi; he started immediately to ask Nurmi a lot of questions, but Nurmi had never been very communicative and answered in monosyllables: Oh, Yes, Na, No, Oh, Ah, and so on.

Finally, after 34 hours' travelling we arrived belatedly in Berlin on 8 May at 9 o'clock in the morning. My young friend Samuelsson got me a room at Hotel Nordland where I had a bath and a very poor breakfast. In the evening we met two young sisters called Paetow, old friends of Samuelsson, who had once worked for a year in Berlin. We went out to a restaurant and had some bottles of good Rhine wine. The eldest sister (about 30 years old) worked in the Foreign Department in Wilhelmsstrasse. She had previously worked as a secretary at the Germany Embassy in London.

She was very anxious to learn about conditions in the U.S.A. – and what public opinion was. I remember that she asked me: "How long do you think the war will last? – "Oh," I said, "it will take about five years." – "Impossible," she said, "our war cannot last more than a year." "Why?" I asked. "World War I lasted four years, and I think this one will be at least as long." "Oh, no," she said, "we *must* end this war inside a year. You see in 1914 Germany was a rich country, but now it is poor. We have to win very quickly otherwise all will be lost."

The next morning we left the Stettiner Bahnhof at 10.30 and reached Sassnitz at 3.45 p.m. There was no ferry boat, and it did not arrive until midnight. We were very stringently searched by the customs and at 3 a.m. left Germany on the Swedish ferry Gustaf V. What a relief! At 6.45 we landed at Trelleborg in Sweden too late for the early train to Stockholm. On the quay we were met by stop-press editions of the newspapers. "Germans invade Holland and Belgium."

There were a few passengers who had been very uneasy all the time we waited for the ferry at Sassnitz, Dutchmen living in Berlin, who had received some kind of advance information and hurried to Sassnitz at the last minute. They certainly looked relieved when they stepped ashore on Swedish soil.

While waiting for the afternoon train I spent a few hours with my colleague Professor Georg Kahlson at Lund and at 11.50 p.m. I finally, much delayed, reached Stockholm where on the platform I was welcomed by Brita, our eldest daughter Helena, and Hugo and Margit Theorell.

Agneta and Johan had been asleep since 8 o'clock. Agneta aged 5, said to her mother: "I remember what he looks like; he combs his hair with water."

While travelling I do not write a diary but often make a few notes each day. I did this in 1940, and on Friday 10 May, the ominous day when Hitler attacked the neutral countries Belgium and Holland, with whom he had signed a non-aggression pact, I wrote "Well, that's the end of this little trip."

CHAPTER XIV

In the deep forests of Wermland investigating the working conditions of lumberjacks.

In 1941 a young man called Gösta Luthman, who had recently graduated from the Polytechnical School of Stockholm, came to see me. He was leading a study group, Wermlands Skogsarbets-studier, to investigate the working conditions of lumberjacks. This young fellow (he was 25) was trained in statistics and calculus, but realized he needed help in studying the physiology of these heavy manual workers. I visited Wermland on several occasions. He had his headquarters in Uddeholm, the centre of one of Sweden's biggest companies in paper, pulp and steel. One of my young assistants, Nils Lundgren, spent several months doing preliminary investigations on the energy metabolism of lumberjacks at the steelworks of Munkfors, which produces the steel for Gillette razor blades.

It was war-time; imports were cut off and food was rationed. With Mrs. Carin Boalt, M.A., at that time working in Professor Abramson's department of Nutrition at the National Institute of Health (Folkhälsan), I started a comparative investigation into individual food consumption among lumberjacks, steelworkers, clerks and their families in the centre of Sweden. I went round different provinces, Wermland, Dalarna and Gästrikland, collecting suitable households to take part in our investigation. I was very efficiently helped in this respect by the Trade Unions and the Clerical Society (T.C.O.). To defray the costs of the investigation, I got part of the money from the Industrial Owners' Association (S.A.F.), and part from the Steelworkers Union ("Metall"). I remember that I went to see the President of the Trade Union

Council (L.O.), August Lindberg, who realized the value of such an investigation and called in Axel Strand who held the powerful position of Treasurer of the L.O. To my great surprise he said no, and walked straight out of the office. But then August Lindberg, noticing my disappointment, smiled and patted me on the shoulder. "Don't worry. We will arrange it another way. Go to 'Metall', the steelworkers' union. I'll call Geijer, their ombudsman." I did this and Mr. Geijer granted me the sum I needed. That day I thus met the three leaders of the L.O., August Lindberg, who was then in office, Axel Strand his successor and Arne Geijer who is President now, men whose role in Sweden's political and social life is comparable to that of the Prime Minister. I was to meet them all again on several occasions.

We were now ready to begin our research. The households in the country districts were supplied with scales. They were given a letter balance to put on the meal table, on which every member of the family weighed everything he ate – the bread, the butter spread on it, and the essential cheese or meat which he placed on top. (Swedish people make themselves such open sandwiches.) All that every individual ate was thus weighed and recorded on special blank forms for a fortnight. A representative of the trade unions or the clerical association then collected all these reports, weighed every person before and after the 2 weeks' survey and recorded their heights and occupations.

In Stockholm, Carin Boalt and I with the aid of special food tables from the Institute of Health then worked out their total consumption of fats, proteins and carbohydrates, minerals and vitamins.

It was of course only an approximate method, but it could be controlled by more direct investigations and proved in practice quite satisfactory. We thus obtained not only a survey of the eating habits in two categories of the working classes and in the middle class, but also an insight into the present state of nutrition

162

among categories of citizens forming some 80% of the Swedish population. We published our result in a book, *Food and Rations*. It was not popular reading as it contained a mass of tables and diagrams with English text and a summary in English. However, the publishers sold 60 copies to the Department of Agriculture in the U.S.A. alone and the book was soon sold out.

The lumberjacks were, of course, found to have the highest energy metabolism, and their heavy work needed an average of 5500 calories per day. In 1942 their total rations, with all their special supplements, did not amount to more than 4000 calories – no wonder that they complained. Their union arranged a meeting at the Stockholm's Concert Hall where their representative told the representative of the authorities responsible for rationing that the lumberjacks could not work a full week; Thursday afternoon they had finished their rations and had to go home. The official responsible for rationing told them that they had more supplementary rations than any other category and that they must be content with what they had. Then I went up on the platform and made it clear that a man who has to do a heavy day's work needing 5500 calories a day cannot produce more than about 60 per cent of his industrial output on only 4000 calories.

Among the audience was Tage Erlander, state secretary in the Social Department, and Olof Söderström, a lawyer on the State Food Commission. These men were both university trained men, and understood the force of my arguments. Sweden was cut off from nearly all imports of fuel oil, and coal imports were very limited. We had to rely on the products of our forests. They understood the imperative need to supply the lumberjacks with adequate additional rations.

Gösta Luthman needed more help from Nils Lundgren and me in his important investigations into lumberjacks' working conditions. We worked out a plan for these studies which included two independent methods of calculating their energy metabolism for different parts of their work – felling, cutting, the barking, etc. – in order to calculate their physical efficiency.

We outlined our plans for an expedition to the forests of Wermland and after consulting the head of Uddeholm's forestry department, Gösta Wesslén and Luthman, I asked for the large sum of 350,000 Crowns for 2 years. It was granted partly by S.A.F., the Industrial Owners' Association and by L.O., the Trade Union Council. We thus had the support of these two powerful bodies who between themselves decided the economic life of Sweden. I was called to a meeting of the Board of the S.A.F. in their fine building on Blasieholmen, facing the Royal Palace across the North River. I made a short summary of our methods of investigation. There were about twenty members assembled, all leaders of Sweden's biggest industrial companies; I had to answer a few questions and then finally the chairman, Torsten Hérnod, head of the Swedish Cellulose Company, said: "Well, now that you have been provided with all this money I suppose in two years you will have solved all our problems." He looked somewhat bewildered when I quite frankly said, "Oh no, all scientific investigations lead only to the creation of new interesting problems which themselves urgently need a solution."

Feeling very happy, I applied for leave from my post as reader at Karolinska Institutet and with Nils Lundgren and a young girl trained in gas analysis arrived in September 1943 with our instruments at a little farm called Lilleäng belonging to Uddeholm Company. The tenant who was both farmer and lumberjack was a very co-operative man who helped us a lot. During the first month we installed ourselves in an empty house where we slept and cooked our meals while two out-buildings were erected in the middle of a neighbouring forest where the subjects of our research were going to fell the trees. I had to attend to a great many practical details. First we had to install electricity in the farm and the huts, which were generously put at our disposal by the Board

One of our subjects at work, equipped with a Douglas bag.

of Labour; its General Director Walberg was very helpful indeed. In a short time we were able to move into the huts, one of which served as living quarters for our subjects, and the other as a laboratory. Our laboratory assistant Stina Flygare rented a room from the farmer, Olsson. Nils Lundgren and I slept in the laboratory hut.

Our subjects, six strong and experienced young fellows from Wermland, Dalarna, and Ångermanland, started work. With the aid of two technical assistants, Mr. Lund and Olsson's young son, we measured their oxygen consumption during the different stages of felling, cutting, barking, etc. The huge Douglas' rubber bags, filled with the air that had been breathed out, were carried into the laboratory, the volume was measured in a gas meter; samples of the air were analysed by Miss Stina Flygare all day long and often until late at night. The Facit calculating machine rattled away, giving us the results. It was a very busy and interesting

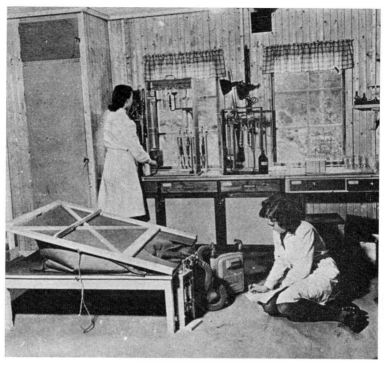

In the laboratory cabin the Douglas bags are emptied through a gas meter and samples of the collected expired air are analysed for content of oxygen and carbon dioxide by Miss Stina Flygare (near the window).

life there in the deep forests of Wermland, ten miles from the nearest grocery store and railway station. In the laboratory we had a bicycle ergometer on which we let the subjects work, recording their pulse rate by an electrical device. Measuring their oxygen consumption against the pulse rate gave us a good index of their physical condition.

My principal aim was to find out what characterizes the most efficient worker, to discover how you can get the most for the least bodily effort. To do this Luthman and his engineers constructed ergometers on which we could accurately measure the physical

166

work while we were measuring the oxygen consumption of the subject; and thus we calculated the energy expenditure of the body in calories while working.

We could calculate the energy expenditure in forestry work and record each worker's output; as it was valued in money we could thus find the relation between his earnings (they were all paid by piecework) and his energy expenditure. The pure physical efficiency which we calculated from the experiments on our working machines varied fairly little among our physically fit subjects, but the relations between their earnings and their energy expenditure varied a great deal. One of the most powerfully built workers showed low figures for the relation between his earnings and his energy expenditure, while a slender young man from Wermland, whom the forester considered a lazy worker, showed the highest earnings in relation to his physical output.

The conclusion was obvious. It is, of course, essential to have strong muscles but to be a really efficient lumberjack you have to have intelligence to organize your work properly. The lumberjack has to do that for himself; it is not like a factory, where he is told how to go about his work. Lumberjacking is an individual job, requiring intelligence for its proper organization. Formerly, the bright young boys went into industry in the towns or the villages, while the dull ones stayed home and worked in the forests. Now we know that it should be the other way round.

We had a wonderful life up there in the forest. We worked very hard in order to be free for weekend excursions in the beautiful countryside of Wermland, with its vast forests and hundreds of lakes. We also had quite a few visitors like the leaders of S.A.F., L.O., the Government's Forestry Department and the Director of the Uddeholm Company. They were very interested in our work, to which they all contributed financially, and they were very good friends although they all fought bitterly at the annual battle over the worker's wages, long, wearing debates lasting sometimes for weeks, and going on till five in the morning.

The outcome often depended upon which side could best survive staying up night after night. These debates and round table conferences at Saltsjöbaden between the Trade Union Council and the S.A.F., the industrial owners, created the industrial stability which has characterized Sweden since the 1930s. Thanks to the great authority of the Trade Union Presidents and the strength of the unions, we have been saved from all the wild-cat strikes which have been so disastrous in many other countries. The Social Democratic Government has also played its part, as it introduced very effective legislation regulating industrial life. Britain's Prime Minister Mr. Wilson tried to do this, but he was not strong enough and the British trade unions do not have leaders who recognize the necessity for it.

Nils Lundgren and I were very happy indeed during those 3 years in Wermland. We got to know our lumberjacks well. They were all without exception "nature's gentleman", as the English say; we became very good friends and we produced a long series of interesting results. Nils Lundgren, Gösta Luthman and I wrote a massive report which was printed in book form: *Heavy Manual Work – a study of lumbering*. Richly illustrated from our research, it was for a time used as a textbook at the Forestry High School.

In 1948 Nils Lundgren received his M.D. degree, after having defended his excellent dissertation – a whole book on lumberjacks. He continued his research for some years at Albequerque in New Mexico, and then went to Calcutta, where he was head of a department of Industrial Physiology at the All India Institute of Health. He is now a professor at the Swedish State Institute of Industrial Medicine. After the first year I could leave most of the research activity in his hands. He was especially well suited to this kind of research; he was skilled in physiological methods, he was athletic, and scrupulously methodical and conscientious.

The workers loved him. He also was wise enough to ask for advice from people like Professor Eric Hohwü Christensen at G.I.H. [1] specializing in the physiology of muscular exercise, who helped him a lot.

In order that our studies of the lumberjack's nutrition and eating habits should be of more general interest and not influenced by food-rationing we were all exempted from rationing, which was of course a blessing, and for this we were very grateful to my friend Olof Söderström, who in 1943 succeeded Bo Hammarsköld, an elder brother of Dag, the former U.N. Secretary, as general director of the State Food Commission. Our results made it possible for me to help him to make a calculation of the nutritional needs of the Swedish population. Söderström had an extraordinary capacity for work. His working day was often 18 hours, but he still found time for his friends. Tage Erlander once called him "Sweden's best civil servant".

One Sunday morning when Professor Ulf von Euler and Brita were visiting us, a local family with six children from 6 to 16 years old came and entertained us with songs sung beautifully in three-part harmony. They were given coffee and cookies and were delightful. They ran a farm deep in the forest, about 15 miles from us, a nice bicycle ride away. They bore the family name Lloyd, and their ancestor was a well-known and very rich Scotsman, who for many years went bear-hunting in Wermland in the early part of the nineteenth century. He had affairs with quite a few of the pretty daughters in the county and one of the results was the great-grandfather of this family. Another natural son of this old bear – hunter was Dr. C. J. Anderson, a great scientist and explorer. The ageing hunter wanted to adopt him, and give him his name, but refused, pointing out that C. J. Ander-

---

[1] Institute for Gymnastic's and Athletic's.

son was now a well-known and respected name in the scientific world and he had no reason to change it.

We had a very good time; the small river was full of crayfish, we often saw elks, the kings of the Swedish forests, and out on the roads, which were only dirt tracks, one often saw capercailzies, black cocks and grey hens who pecked the small stones on the road to grind the food in their stomachs. We also saw foxes trying to break into Olsson's poultry house. About 5 miles from us at the top of a hill lived a widow in an old farm settlement, who had grown rather fat and now weighed 220 pounds. It was 5 years since she had last visited the village and grocery store. She lived with her household of three lumberjacks on the products of her small farm, a few cows, goats and chickens. Rationing had not affected her. She churned her butter, made her cheese, milled her flour; cured pork with meat and potatoes, and bread and butter were their daily diet. The only shortages were coffee and sugar, which were heavily rationed. But we (and many others, I suppose) readily exchanged their coffee and sugar ration coupons for her fine butter and delicate full cream cheese. She was a woman with a very jolly disposition, and was a great gossip. We always enjoyed the hour's walk up the path to her cottage (there was no road) and in winter we went on skis, of course.

It was a wonderful life, and a great change from Stockholm and my naval service each summer. My readers may find it odd that I, a specialist in neurophysiology, turned to nutrition and the physiology of muscular exercise. There were reasons for this. First, we all wanted to prove ourselves useful to our country during the war. Hugo Theorell, for example, started, with Dr. Hans Davide, a series of experiments to produce a specific antibiotic against tuberculosis. After an enormous amount of work, they seemed on the threshold of success. It worked beautifully on guinea pigs who are very sensitive to T.B., but required, unfortunately,

170

too large a dose in man, doses which were so locally damaging to the tissues that they could not be given with safety.

Perhaps more or less unconsciously I had a desire to show that I could work in another field of physiology. I had previously been declared incompetent to a chair in physiology at G.C.I. where I had taught for 11 years. The three referees were, of course, formally correct, but I felt the need to demonstrate that I was quite capable of conducting research in their field as well. I do not consider the years I spent in industrial physiology as wasted. It gave Sweden an expert in that field, Nils P. V. Andersson, and it gave me a training in administration too, which was very valuable when, in 1946, I had to develop a new institute of physiology at the Veterinary School; in spite of the fact that it was rather odd that I, who perhaps at that time was the only Swedish physiologist who had experience in human physiological research, should have to turn to veterinary physiology. I have never regretted these years in the forests; and occasionally I had time to sneak back to my rather awful room beneath the Stockholm Mortuary to do some nerve physiology. *On revient toujours à ses premières amours.* I had a free life, free from faculty meetings and university quarrels and intrigues. I also got to know some very interesting and worthwhile people.

CHAPTER XV

The long path to a Professor's chair.

At the end of the 1930s three chairs in physiology became open to application: at Lund University following the retirement of Torsten Thunberg; at Stockholm after Hans Gertz died in 1938; and at Uppsala after Gustaf Göthlin retired. I did not apply for the chair at Lund, as I knew that it was destined for Georg Kahlson who was actually appointed there in 1939. I sent in my papers for the chair at Karolinska Institutet, although I knew that it was destined for Ulf von Euler; there was a certain value in being considered for a professorship.

The appointment of a professor in Sweden follows a kind of court proceeding. When a chair is vacant the candidates must send in a full list of qualifications, including a birth certificate, a list of scientific publications and at least three copies of all printed papers or manuscripts, to be scrutinized by three or more referees, who are specialists chosen by the Faculty. They are supposed to examine and write an extensive report on all the candidates' scientific papers, finally placing the candidates in order of merit. The reports should reach the Faculty within 6 months, but very often the referees ask for an extension date. These reports are then opened at a Faculty meeting, and copies sent to each member and the candidates. Then the Faculty discusses the reports and selects a candidate, that is, sends a proposal to the Consistorium, made up of elected members from all the Faculties of the University. This body discusses the reports and puts the candidates in order of merit, and then hands the papers to the Chancellor of the Swedish University. This high-ranking official discusses the matter with his Council and sends the papers to the Government. The Minister of Education studies them with his secretary; the matter is then brought to the "Statsrådsberedningen" and finally one candidate is appointed by the Government, in a session presided over by the King. After some weeks he receives a beautiful sheet of hand-made paper confirming his appointment, with the King's signature appended.

This is a very lengthy procedure which may take more than a year, and sometimes 2 years when the qualifications of the candidates have been fairly equal and for that reason the choice has been difficult, so the different authorities have to work hard and long to reach a decision. Often the proceedings are excessively prolonged, because the candidates have the right to appeal against every decision. Appeals may even start after the Faculty's election of referees. A candidate can appeal to the Government complaining that there is no one among the referees capable of evaluating his research, or that a referee has been co-author of too many papers by one of the candidate's rivals; or that he is the father-in-law of one of them. Appeals like these have actually been made. The most usual thing is that one or more of the candidates who have not been short-listed by the referees appeal against their reports, accusing them of mistakes and ignorance in lengthy articles which sometimes are even printed in the daily newspapers. The papers are then sent back to the Faculty for a second reading, so many months can elapse while appeals are made at every stage until the Chancellor becomes involved. Finally, when the proceedings are solely in the hands of the Government, supporters run backwards and forwards between the Government offices trying to persuade the Minister to make the "right" choice.

There has been much debate about the feasibility of introducing a better system of appointment. It is very difficult in a democratic country. The pity of it is that the procedure embitters so many good scientists, and this was especially so in my youth, when the number of chairs was very limited. Today it is much easier, as the Research Councils can now take care of any good scientist who does not obtain an ordinary chair. In the old days it was sometimes a catastrophe for a scientist who was qualified for a chair at the age of 50. It was impossible for him to find another living as he could not, at that age, return to a lectureship with a limited tenure.

I went through three such bitter fights before I was finally appointed professor and head of the department of Physiology and Pharmacology at the Royal Veterinary School in May 1946. I would rather not record these bitter years, although some of the incidents were quite comic, when for instance, a Professor of Moral Philosophy within the Faculty of Divinity declared one candidate fully competent to hold a chair although three of the four referees had found him incompetent. The fourth referee was a local professor, whose own competence was very dubious.

I finally ended up at a place where I could do just the work I wanted. I do not believe any other place would have suited me so well. One night in May 1945, when I was having my little after-dinner nap, the telephone woke me. I heard the voice of a woman colleague, Dr. Elsa Ulfsparre. "Hello, Professor," she said. "Hello, my Princess," I replied. "Thank you," she said, "but I mean what I say." "Oh, but so do I," I added. And then she explained that she had heard on the radio newsreel that the Government had given me the title of Professor. I rushed in to Brita who was putting our son Johan to bed and told her. I ran down and bought an evening paper and there it was, so we decided to take a taxi to the Southern Hospital to tell my mother. We found her in relatively good condition and broke the news. "Oh, that's excellent, my son," she said, "now I can request that you do not put your hands in your pockets all the time you are speaking."

A few days later I went up to the Minister of Education in his office in the Chancery beneath the Royal Palace. It was Georg Andrén, Professor of Political Science at Gothenburg. He was a very handsome man in his early sixties. He told me the following story: "When, a few weeks ago, I took over from Bagge, I went through drawers of this desk and found an application dating from 1940 and signed by a long list of names, physiologists, professors and other scientists, who had asked the Government to give you a Professor's title. As a member of Riksdagen (Swedish Parliament) I have lived for many winters in the same little family hotel as your mother, whom I admire greatly. I knew that she was seriously ill, so I told my state secretary to put forward this application, as my first act in the next session of the Cabinet. How is your mother? I hope she is not in pain." "Oh, no," I said, and told him how she had congratulated me. "Well, that is her own inimitable way, and very appropriate to a lady of her strong character," he said, smiling.

CHAPTER XVI

Teaching at a Veterinary College. — A discovery by a young veterinarian. — German visitors.

When I first came to Stockholm in 1909, the Veterinary School was situated on Östermalm, close to my old grammar school on Karlavägen. The buildings were surrounded by a large garden filled with apple, pear and cherry trees. We used to steal the apples in September, climbing over the high wooden fence around the garden. It was a busy thoroughfare with all kinds of horse-drawn carriages and horsemen in uniform or in civilian clothes taking their mounts to the Institute for veterinary care, or to get new steel shoes. We used to hear the sound of hammering from the forge. In 1912 the Veterinary School moved into new buildings, situated in lovely surroundings by Lake Brunnsviken opposite Haga Palace, a Royal summer residence now used to accommodate foreign visitors like Kruschev.

In 1944 Vilhelm Sahlstedt, one of the founders of our Physiological Society in Stockholm (in 1919), came to see me and told me that he was reaching retiring age. He kindly suggested I should apply for the new chair of Physiology and Pharmacology at the Veterinary School, his department of Chemistry and Physiology having been split into two separate departments. So I handed in my credentials at the appropriate time – but so alas did all the other young men. The referees were divided in their decision, and so was the Veterinary Faculty, and so too was the Board of the Veterinary School. I do not blame them. One of the referees who in a previous competition had declared me incompetent now put me first on his list. My competitors, some older, some younger than I, were all well-trained physiologists: one had friends in the Government. The Dean of the School was against my election; he wanted the post to go to a veterinarian. The papers were sent back and forth at each stage; the competitors appealed against those referees who did not put them high enough in order of merit. But the candidates fought only against the referees and the professors; we very loyally did not fight each other, at least as far as I can remember. Finally the Government came to a decision. On 2 May 1946 I was appointed, and a process which had taken nearly 2 years had come to an end. I do not think that the long fight caused any lasting bitterness among the participants. All my competitors have reached positions which I am quite sure they would not exchange for mine, nor I for theirs.

Some days after my appointment I went to see the Dean and Professor of Veterinary Surgery. He was sitting at his desk in his little office, a tall, handsome fellow. He was a skilled surgeon, a competent speaker and a man of great resource. He looked up over his glasses, stepped forward, shook hands very heartily, and welcomed me to the school.

"Now that the King has made his decision, I suggest that we forget our differences," he said, smiling. "As an elder colleague I would like to give you a word of advice. Do not plan any retaliation . . . it just does not pay." He looked quite pleased when I nodded in agreement. I later understood what he meant. The Faculty was divided into two factions. The Dean was the leader of the majority party which, however, was somewhat labile. He did not want me to join the opposition. But in spite of the fact I mostly voted with the other party, headed by the anatomist Axel Palmgren and the Professor of Veterinary Medicine for non-Ruminants, Birger Carlström, two very active members who spoke out freely and frankly, I became very friendly with the gallant Dean Forssell. One of his many famous brothers was Gösta Forssell, my teacher in Radiology at Karolinska Institutet, and founder of the worldknown Radiumhemmet for the cure of cancer. Another was Nils Forssell, an historian, who held the position of secretary of the Idun

Society for science and arts, which numbered among its most active members the Crown Prince, the present King, Gustaf VI Adolf. So we met the Dean and his wife quite often in social life; we also became neighbours at Experimentalfältet when he retired as Dean in 1957.

Professor Sahlstedt took me around the old premises allotted to my department. The laboratories were very badly equipped except in chemistry, which was Sahlstedt's primary discipline. He used to ask the question: What is the difference between a Veterinarian and a Quack? The answer is – chemistry.

He told me that he had saved the large sum of 10,000 Crowns ($2000) during the last 10 years. He had worked hard as Dean and had abandoned all his scientific activity. He nearly fell backwards in astonishment when I told him that I had made detailed lists of the scientific equipment which I needed urgently and which would cost 175,000 Crowns. He was not the only one who was astonished. Most of the members of the Faculty shook their heads when I presented my list of requirements and my request for so much money, but in the end they consented and passed it on to the Board for submission to the Government, which reduced the sum to 130,000 Crowns which Parliament finally agreed to give me.

It was equally urgent that the premises should be modernized. There was no A.C. power, only D.C., and I needed A.C. for my research. I had to approach the State Building Department, the General Director of which was an architect, Wejke. He was always engaged, but after some hours in the waiting room I was allowed in to see him. All he said was: "I have no time for you and your lab, as I have to look at the designs of the new buildings for the Academy of Music. Parliament will allocate the money next Spring." "But my laboratory must be rebuilt this summer, before I start the term in September," I said. "The Government must pass a bill to Parliament at its Autumn session." He looked very uncomfortable and without saying a word turned round and walked out of his office. My audience was over. A few hours later my lab phone rang, and the secretary announced that General Director Wejke wanted to speak to Professor Zotterman. I was surprised. "Hello," he said. "I am sorry I was so busy when you came to see me. How can I help you?" Well, he did help – the lab was completely rebuilt for about 100,000 Crowns. It was not quite ready in September, but I could at least start my research and teaching.

Besides me, there were only three members of my department: an assistant, an amanuensis and a lab servant. I managed to get young Carl G. Schmiterlöw to come over from Karolinska Institutet as an assistant. He was a well-trained young physiologist with a special interest in pharmacology. I had once been his teacher and examiner in physiology. He quickly advanced to reader and then to Professor of Pharmacology, and is now the Dean of the Veterinary School. The amanuensis was chosen from among the students each year. The lab man was an old fellow who, in the active days of Professor Sahlstedt, had made quite a few pieces of apparatus in the workshop, but had since become an alcoholic. He died a few years later.

The first things I did in May were to buy modern machinery for the workshop in the basement, and to appoint an instrument maker. I wanted to build up the new laboratory round the workshop. I was extremely lucky to find the very best man, a young instrument maker, Ingvar Anderson, who was willing to help me for a salary of 500 Crowns per month. There was no money allocated for him, but I paid him out of the research money which I received from the Anderson Fund at Karolinska Institutet. The necessary machinery for the workshop I bought on credit so that Ingvar Anderson could start making the kymographs and other apparatus for the lab. I was fortunate to get such a skilled instrument maker; after a year the Dean helped me to persuade the

Government to give him the post of instrument maker of the school with a better salary.

In February 1947 I was thus, with the help of Schmiterlöw, able to give the first practical class in physiology and the students seemed to be quite interested in doing experiments on frogs, rabbits and cats and even goats. The senior students, however, who did not know me well, demonstrated against me – they did not like my appointment, because I was not a veterinarian. They even wrote to their monthly journal and complained that I was teaching neurophysiology. "What use is neurophysiology to veterinarians?" somebody wrote. To this I replied that I believed that the domestic animals were quite as much dependent on their nervous system as we are and that, as far as I was aware, animals also suffered from diseases of their nervous system – is not distemper a disease which particularly affects the dog's nervous system?!

In the Faculty I made the following statement: "I see my principal duty, besides teaching veterinary students physiology, is to train a few veterinarians to be expert physiologists." The demonstration and other activities against me soon stopped. The veterinary Faculty, the Board and particularly the young Minister of Agriculture, Gunnar Sträng, were all very generous to me. Sträng's predecessor, Mr. Per Edvin Sköld, started a parliamentary committee in 1947 to create better economic conditions and better research facilities for the Veterinary, Forestry and Agricultural colleges of Sweden. This committee under the skilled leadership of the former State Secretary, Governor Bertil Fallenius, worked quickly and two years later the Government passed a bill to Parliament which would entirely revolutionize research and teaching at our Veterinary School. It meant a great deal to me as it divided my teaching duties, adding a new chair in pharmacology, a readership in physiology, a lab assistant, etc. From a teaching staff of three in 1946–47 the number now increased to nine, and the technical staff increased from one to six in all.

180

In the Spring of 1949 C. G. Schmiterlöw defended his thesis for his M.D. degree at Karolinska Institutet and thus became competent to the readership in physiology. He was soon declared competent to the new chair of pharmacology in 1950. Thus I was given more time for research.

During a visit to Göttingen in 1948 I became acquainted with a young assistant in physiology from Heidelberg, Dr. Herbert Hensel, who had made some nice experiments on the temperature senses using psychophysical methods. I invited him to join me in Stockholm in 1949–50, when I could provide him with a temporary lectureship. None of the veterinarians was at that time competent enough for such a post. Hensel's arrival was a very good thing for me and my group of young postgraduate students. I had been able to renew my arsenal of apparatus, some of which had been made by a visitor, Dr. Ing. Jan Friedrich Tönnies, who had come out of a French prison after having suffered a severe attack of diphtheria. Poor fellow, he was very thin and pale when he arrived in Stockholm, but he soon recovered and I owe much to him for his ingenious help in building up my electronic gadgets, amplifiers, cathode-ray oscilloscopes, stimulators, etc. Herbert Hensel was also an excellent designer, and helped our instrument maker to build a very fine film camera. Finally in 1950 I succeeded in finding a skilled electronics man, a senior student at the Poly-technic School (K.T.H.) called Lennart Ström, who had a thorough theoretical training which was to prove extremely valuable to our research.

In 1947 our laboratory had several foreign visiting scientists. With the help of the Swedish Institute, a few German and Austrian physiologists came to Sweden to recuperate after the very hard post-war years and to read current literature, from which they had been isolated for nearly 10 years. Professor Rickard Jung came from Freiburg and Professor Adolf Jarisch from Innsbruck.

Just after they left, in the autumn of 1947, Professor Georg von Békésy left Hungary for Stockholm. He started work at the Polytechnical High School with Professor Laurent, designing a new audiometer for the testing of hearing. He came on to me and we began some research on the acoustic nerve using needle electrodes in order to record from single fibres of the cochlear nerve of the cat.

As a matter of fact these needles were actually ordinary sewing needles which I enamelled except for the tip, which must measure, let us say, one-hundredth of a millimetre. Similar needles had previously been used by Granit to record from – as he believed – single nerve fibres in the eye and by Galambos and H. Davies in the U.S.A. for recording from cochlear nerve fibres. To our great surprise we managed in our first experiment to lead off from a single element. But how is it possible, we asked, to prick single fibres of a diameter of less than one-hundredth of a millimetre with such gross needles? We repeated our experiments a few times before Békésy lost interest. Being a physicist, he could not understand why we were not able to make successful experiments every day, as you can if you use dead matter. After a few unsuccessful experiments he would quit. I sometimes got bad bleedings, but misfortunes happen to physiologists; we are used to it and must cultivate patience. But although we never finished our experiments, or wrote any official report, we were quite certain that when we succeeded we were not pricking single nerve fibres, but single nerve *cell bodies* six times the diameter of the fibre. It was soon proved conclusively that we were right. My earlier associate Bo Gernandt went to H. Davis in St. Louis and told him about our theory. Whether he and Galambos already had the same idea, I cannot tell, but a year later they announced that they had discovered quite a few nerve cell bodies in the cochlear nerve where they inserted needle electrodes. A year later our friend William Rushton from Cambridge demonstrated, while working

Aladar and Margit Beznak.

in Granit's lab in Stockholm, that Granit had recorded the activity of huge cell bodies in the inner layer of the retina. Well, it made sense, and fortunately it did not affect the validity of Granit's results, as these cellbodies discharge in single nerve fibres in the cochlear and optic nerve respectively. It is vital for me to state this.

Our Hungarian friends Margit and Aladar Beznak, whom we had invited in the autumn of 1937 to see their friend and compatriot, Albert Szent-Györgyi, receiving his Nobel Prize, came back for a short visit after the war. They had had a terrible time towards the end of the war but managed to stay in their laboratory. We were able to send them dried milk powder and other foods with the first Red Cross expedition which reached Budapest after the Siege. They were almost starved at that time, particularly for protein. They wrote to tell me how they felt their brains recover the power to think after a few glasses of milk and their failing memories return to normal. It was a very touching letter. During the Siege of Budapest, I received a cable: Please try to get Professor Korossyi Swedish citizenship. In order to save Jewish scientists and members of other professions, the Swedish diplomats in Budapest had given these poor people citizenship; among them was Szent-Györgyi. I phoned immediately our Foreign Office, where I spoke to a young attaché. He said that it was too late: the cable link to Budapest was cut. However, I called the Telegraph Office. "Can you take a telegram for Budapest?" I asked. "Yes," announced the lady. "Are you sure?" "Oh yes," she replied, "I have just sent one off, and we are still receiving telegrams." So I dictated a telegram on my own responsibility: *Swedish Foreign Office grant Korossyi Swedish Citizenship – Zotterman*. "Necessity follows no law" is a Swedish proverb. They could have sent me to prison for it or perhaps dismissed me from my post – I did not care – the important thing was to send the telegram. But, more important still, it worked. Old Professor Korossyi was saved from a certain death. A year later I received a long, very touching letter from him giving me the details of his escape. His son visited us a few years later.

Two years later I received a telegram from Vienna. "We are here, the Swedish Legation is helping us to get to Sweden – Beznak." We had realized for a long time that their situation in Hungary was precarious. Beznak had more or less voluntarily left his chair in Budapest and taken a post as director of the Biological Research Station at the Balaton Lake. Old Professor Mansfield whom the Russians had found when they came to the concentration camp at Auschwitz had taken his place in Budapest. In a Russian film from Auschwitz we had seen Professor Mansfeld in the striped clothes of a prisoner . . . one of the few who were alive and who were not starved beyond recovery . . . a very few.

A few days later we welcomed Margit and Aladar Beznak to

Stockholm. The Rockefeller Foundation granted them a fellowship and for a year he continued his research on nervous humoral transmission in my laboratory and Margit was in Hugo Theorell's laboratory at the Nobel Medical Institute. He then obtained a post as university lecturer in Manchester, where they stayed for a few years. Finally he was appointed professor of physiology at Ottawa in Canada. We visited them there in 1958, shortly after the Hungarian uprising. They were very busy and happy receiving and helping Hungarian refugees who had escaped from the Russians. Aladar was a very gentle person of great charm. A great Hungarian patriot, his English postgraduate education, his liberal views and his democratic principles forced him to live in exile for the last 15 years of his life.

He did not desert his country until it was absolutely necessary. They were about to put him in jail for alleged treachery. He could not possibly have committed any crime: he was the most gentle person I knew, with a personality similar in many ways to George de Hevesy, who likewise came to Sweden. Aladar left us suddenly in 1964. He was succeeded in the chair at Ottawa by his brave wife Margit von Beznak.

In February 1948 I advertised in the small *Veterinarian Monthly* that there would be a new post as assistant in my department from 1 July. A few days later a young veterinarian came to my office. He was a tall, slender fair-haired young man, who bowed low to me when he introduced himself as Bengt Andersson, *pro tempore* District Veterinarian at Gellivare, high up in Swedish Lapland, above the Arctic Circle. He had had no previous experience in physiology but he had gained very high marks in his examinations. He made me understand in his shy way that he longed to do research and that he was anxious to start as soon as possible – as early as next month. Well, I was anxious to have somebody to help me in my own research, so I told him to come from 1 April and he did so to the future happiness of both of us. Until

1 July I gave him 300 Crowns a month from my research, which at least paid for his meals.

I had some time previously discovered that the frog had taste fibres which responded to the application of tap water to the tongue, and I invited Bengt Andersson to join me in this research. In a few days he was able to do the nerve preparations himself and after only a month or two I could write up papers with him.

In December Walter Rudolph Hess of Zurich was awarded a Nobel Prize in Physiology or Medicine for his discoveries about the regulatory functions of the middle brain. I had that summer gone through all his principal papers and was very fascinated by his work on hypothalamic function. Using implanted electrodes in different parts of the brain, he was able to elicit by electrical stimulation a great number of reactions of the cat in a fully awake state. Such methods must be gold mines, I thought, for studying the nervous mechanism of animal behaviour and regulatory functions in the living organism.

So I asked Professor Hess whether he would take my young assistant in his laboratory for some months in 1950. I introduced Bengt Andersson to him at a dinner party at our home, the Medical Research Council helped us with a travelling grant and in February 1950 Bengt went to Zurich. He returned after 3 months and immediately started to design electrodes suitable for implanting in the hypothalamic region of the brain of goats. He wanted to study the nervous mechanism of how the milk is let down in the teats of the udder. So he obtained some lactating goats and I will never forget how excited he was when he first demonstrated to me how the milk flowed from the cannulized teats of the goat when he stimulated a certain region of the hypothalamus.

Let me explain the mechanism. A milkmaid always massages the teats before milking, to "let down the milk". Andersson could now show that massaging the teats produced nerve-impulses which ran up to a special group of nerve cells in the hypothalamus near the

186

walls of the third brain ventricle. There these impulses bring into action special cells which send out fibres to the posterior part of the pituitary gland where their endings liberate a substance, a hormone which we now know consists of qamino acids. (It was discovered about this time by Du Vigneaud who was awarded the Nobel Prize in 1955.) This hormone is released in the circulatory blood and forces the smooth muscles in the udder to pass down the milk to the teats.

Bengt Andersson, who is a very quick ambitious worker, was able to defend his thesis for a veterinary Medical Doctor's degree as early as May 1951, and received high honours. Once I told my colleague and friend Hallowel Davis about this discovery. "Oh, I know an old rhyme about that. It goes:

> There was a young lassie of Huddersfield
> Who had a cow that wouldn't yield.
> The reason why she would not yield,
> Was she didn't liked her udders feeled.

So you see it is well known." "Yes, of course, but now we know how it is brought about."

Bengt Andersson was given a readership and was getting on well with a young veterinarian student Stig Larsson, who was helping him. We discussed various problems almost daily. I had an idea that perhaps thirst was elicited from the same area in the hypothalamus. My reason was that we knew, from Basil Verney's research at Cambridge, that the water excretion of the kidney is regulated by an antidiuretic hormone released from the pituitary gland; thus when the body's water content is low these cells are stimulated, resulting in a release of the hormone which works on the kidney in such a way that less water is excreted in the urine. I said to Bengt, "You should see if the goat becomes thirsty when you stimulate the region near the third ventricle."

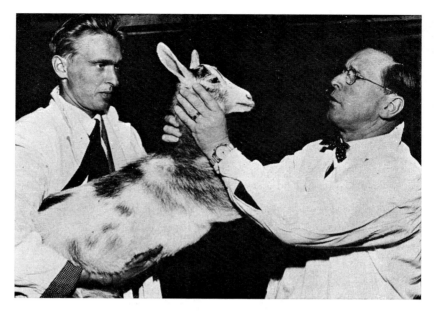

Dr. Bengt Andersson presenting one of his famous goats.

A few days later he came rushing up to my office. "Yngve," he cried out, "You must come down immediately to the lab." So I ran downstairs. There was the goat, with a fine cannula put in through the top of her skull down to the hypothalamus, looking quite at ease, standing quietly near a great barrel of water. "Now, watch when I inject a cubic millimetre of 3% saline to stimulate the region," said Bengt. After a few seconds the goat looked around, went to the barrel and started to drink. The experiment could be repeated several times with the same result; the goat always began to drink. "Beautiful," I said, "you have made a great discovery." "Please Yngve," he said, "you must join me in this research; it is a big thing." "Yes," I said, "you are quite right, but you are the right person to develop it; there is your future."

Later on he adopted electrical stimulation which was less vulnerable to the sensitive nerve cells. He made films of the experiment which show the little goat drinking up to 4 gallons of water, his stomach enormously distended. The next morning the kidneys had excreted it, flooding the lab. What a day it was! One or two days like that in your life are quite enough to keep you going. Nothing in the world gives you more satisfaction than when you suddenly discover a new relation between events hitherto not understood or grasped. Thirst was believed to be produced by dryness in the throat. That was the outcome of some experiments by the great Harvard physiologist Cannon in the 1920s, and you found the theory in all the textbooks. Later we found that the great French physiologist Claude Bernard had very definitely been able to prove in the 1860s that this was not the case. He was inclined to believe that thirst was brought about by dehydration of the brain. At the turn of this century another Frenchman, André Mayer, had made further experiments confirming Claude Bernard's views. Now Bengt Andersson had definitely proved it and moreover he had found the location of these sensitive cells – the thirst centre. Bengt Andersson's discovery was recognized all over the world and young, skilled physiologists from abroad came to work with him. Thirst and its physiological purpose of including intake of water to counteract dehydration of the body became a great subject for research.

I remember I wrote a review of Andersson's discovery in a German journal which started by quoting a verse of the German poet Scheffel from his song "Die drei Dörfer" which I once saw painted on the wall of a famous old Bierstube in Heidelberg:

> Hallohe!
> So wie man's treibt so geht's,
> was liegt an dem Verlurste.
> Man spricht von vielem Trinken stets,
> doch nie vom grossen Durste!

CHAPTER XVII

"An uncut diamond." — English, American and Japanese visitors in our lab.

Having received almost all my scientific training, both pre- and post-graduate, in England, I felt especially pleased when young physiologists from England asked to join me in the 1950s. Professor L. Hemmingway at Leeds wrote to tell me that he wanted to send to me one of his young lecturers, Dr. Eric Neil, to learn our technique in recording from the carotid sinus nerve. "He is an uncut diamond," said one of my English friends. He certainly was a jewel! He arrived with his wife and mother-in-law and a brother-in-law. My efficient secretary managed to find them a suitable furnished apartment where they led a comfortable and quite gay life which seemed rather to stimulate his research in the lab than the reverse. Eric Neil is such a lively person. He was already at

Dr. Eric Neil.

Rune Larsson receives the King's medal from the Dean, Professor
C. G. Schmiterlöw.

that time considered a great scholar and has since become the
author of a very popular textbook. He became the great friend
of everybody in the lab: my secretary, my lab man, Rune Larsson,
my most skilled assistant, our instrument maker Ingvar Andersson,
Dr. Sven Landgren and most of all Dr. Bengt Andersson. It was a
most pleasant and happy life both in and out of the lab and
productive too – although some of us, like Eric, burned the candle
at both ends. He proved useful to us in correcting the English in
our scientific papers. At that period I often sent about ten papers
a year by myself and my visiting scientists to various journals.
Eric Neil and his wife came to work with us on three separate
occasions. He is now Professor of Physiology at the Middlesex
Hospital Medical School in London, and in 1965 was elected
Treasurer of the Union of Physiological Sciences (I.U.P.S.), a great
honour.

Eric and Anne, his pretty wife, a medical practitioner, did me

Dr. Sven Landgren as a "starboy" at a Sancta
Lucia party at the lab, 1950.
(Photo: Herbert Hensel.)

many personal services for which I am very grateful. We were
always welcome in their Highgate home where they entertained
us like royalty, Anne and her mother serving us delicious meals
for which Eric provided excellent wines. After dinner he would
play for us at the piano. He is indeed a gifted person and his two
very pretty and talented daughters lend both colour and atmosphere to their family life.

Another young physiologist was Dr. George Gordon from
Oxford, a tall handsome young fellow with all the qualities
of an Oxford don. His father was professor of English literature at Oxford and President of Magdalen College. He had
himself been to Eton, spoke and wrote beautiful English and
in his parents' house had met many well-known English poets

192

Eric and Anne Neil entertain the author, his wife and daughter Helena at a Stockholm restaurant.

and writers of the 1930s like Priestley, Walpole and Wodehouse. Working with George on the monkey's taste nerves was a pleasure and it was, of course, a great help to have such a master in the English language around when we were writing up our English papers for publication. His charming wife Peggy joined us in December 1962. One day George came to the lab looking very distressed. He had been shopping and suddenly discovered that he had lost his wallet containing about £100. We drove immediately to the city and visited in turn every shop that he had been in. After a while we were lucky enough to find it, for a shop keeper had discovered it on the pavement just outside his shop door and had immediately informed the local police station from where we collected the wallet.

For nearly 10 years, from 1955 onwards, I had Japanese physiologists working with me in my lab. The first one to come was young Susumo Hagiwara, a brilliant scholar. I went to the airport to meet him, but was somewhat late and could not find him. A few minutes later another plane from Copenhagen arrived, but still there was no Hagiwara. I asked an air stewardess from the first plane if there had been a Japanese Professor aboard, but she said No, only a small Japanese boy, so I drove back to the laboratory where my secretary told me that there had just been a phone call from the Japanese Embassy. Dr. Hagiwara had arrived and they were bringing him over to the school.

Hagiwara was indeed small in stature, but as a scientist he is great. He joined me in a piece of research with George Gordon from Oxford on the taste fibres of the rhesus monkey and we enjoyed having him. It was in the autumn, and I often took him with me to pick wild mushrooms in the forests north of Stockholm. His English was not very good – it was the first time he had left Japan– but it quickly improved. We liked having him as our guest for dinner at home; he could easily wear my old tails that I had in 1919 at the Nobel Feast. His teacher, Katsuki, who came from Tokyo, also spent a month with us in 1957, and he was followed by Jurio Iriuchijima, also a very talented and skilful young man, who helped me in recording from single non-myelinated nerve fibres mediating cold, warmth and pain. We wrote three papers together. Iriuchijima was the son of a general and had been brought up in the ancient Japanese tradition, and was quite exquisitely polite. He quickly learned to speak fairly good English; he was interested in opera and he even gave my secretary Mrs. Gördis Lilliesköld lessons in Culbertson bridge. The last month he was with us he often received fat letters containing photographs of different Japanese girls, as his parents were anxious for him to marry. A few weeks after he had left us for a visit to the U.S.A., I received a postcard from Yosemity Valley in California, telling us that he was there on his honeymoon. He had met his wife for the first time in the docks of San Francisco when she arrived from Japan. They had been married by proxy in Japan. We met his wife, a beautiful girl, who was the daughter of a medical practitioner, in 1965 in Tokyo by which time they had a son and seemed very happy indeed.

He was succeeded by a dental physiologist, Dr. Masai Funakoshi from Osaka's Dental school, a young, gay man who surprised us all by singing the Sancta Lucia song in Swedish on 13 December. We worked together on the nerves to the pulp of the teeth, the fibres conveying pain. We heated the tooth and recorded the pain nerves sending out impulses as soon the temperature at the pulp border was raised above 45°C. We had thermopiles at the pulp-dentine border to record the temperature simultaneously with the impulse traffic in the nerve fibres from the pulp. We found that when drilling the tooth the nerve endings at the pulp dentine border started signalling when the heat of the drill had raised the temperature to 45°. Nowadays most dentists use drills with cold water squirting on the tooth, thus preventing unnecessary pain. When the drill comes too near the pulp, however, it mechanically stimulates the pain fibres, thus producing pain. We were able to present this piece of research in London at a Symposium on the Sensitivity of Dentine at the Royal Society of Medicine. It was organized by Professor Anderson and I was in the chair. It was an excellent meeting, with a good deal of first-class papers, for example one by Donald Scott, Jr. He had invented a new method which enabled him to record from single nerve endings in the tooth. It was a very open question whether these nerve endings were situated in the dentine itself or whether they were at the pulp dentine border, the dental canals acting as conducting micro-tubuli to endings at the pulp-dentine border, as I suggested. The latter fitted in very well with the experiments by Funakoshi and with my experiments and also with the work of several anatomists who were present at the meeting.

Masai Funakoshi was indeed most skilled and was enormously

active in the lab; he went back to Japan with his name on no fewer than five papers and was promoted to associate professor. We visited him and his boss, Motakawa, in Osaka in 1965. Unfortunately it was a very short visit for after only a few hours we had to rush back to our hotel where we were locked in very early for the night; the doors and windows were made fast as a typhoon was sweeping the city. But that is another story.

Another very distinguished visiting research worker was Professor Jikei Konishi from the University of the Mi Prefecture at Tsu in Japan, some 200 miles south of Tokyo, in the centre of its pearl fishery.

In 1959 I tried to make recordings from taste nerves of fish in La Jolla, California, but with very little success. Konishi suggested that we should try the carp fish. I succeeded, thanks to my friend Professor Sven Runnström, Head of the Fresh Water Fish Laboratory, in getting suitable carp fish for our experiments though I cannot go into details about our findings. But it may be interesting to tell you how surprised I was one day when Konishi put some of his saliva on the palatal organ of the fish and there was a strong response from its taste nerves. Saliva is tasteless to us or to other mammals. I believed at first that it was due to potassium rhodanide, present in Konishi's saliva as he was a chain smoker. But as my own saliva had the same effect that idea was quickly abandoned, as I had not then smoked for 15 years. The question remained, what substance in the saliva produced the taste response of the fish? Konishi started a long series of chemical work on saliva which he finished in Japan a year later and it was a fine piece of chemical detection. It turned out to be a phospholipid, a substance present in milk, meat, earth worms, etc. It was very interesting to find that there were special taste fibres which responded specifically to this substance, which is present in all kind of foods which fish find palatable. It is yet another example of biological evolution. We also enjoyed making this discovery as it

196

shed a new light on the old habit of spitting on the bait which I always had done, believing it to be a sort of magic!

Jikei Konishi was a wonderfully skilled, earnest and capable scientist and we became close friends. We spent two days with him in Tsu in 1965. His charming wife, a daughter of an owner of a silk factory, took us up to see the factory where the cocoons were spun. It was a most interesting visit. We spent a day looking at the Amas, the strong Japanese pearl diving girls, but had to rush for our train rather suddenly because a typhoon was passing with its centre through the town of Tsu. That was the last time I was ever to see my dear friend Jikei Konishi, standing on the platform with his beautiful kimona-clad wife, their children waving to us as the train left. Next year we heard that he died after an abdominal operation. He was a chain smoker, and heavy smoking no doubt killed this brilliant research worker, a most charming man. I felt as if I had lost a brother.

All these fine Japanese scientists lived during their stay in Stockholm in a room in the laboratory which, on its door, carried the sign Professor Emeritus, a fairly large room with two sofas which could be turned into beds. (It had also a wash stand and there was a bath room in the basement of the building outside the lecture hall which they used frequently.) We were afraid that they would find life very monotonous in the lab, particularly in the long evenings, but they never complained. On the contrary, they nearly all told me afterwards that their year in Stockholm was the happiest of their lives. Perhaps that was just Japanese courtesy. However, I used to bring them home at least once a week for dinner at Experimentalfältet and took them in our car on Sundays out into the country. They lived very ascetically as they do in Japan. In the tearoom they used the refrigerator and the electric stove for preparing their food, and could thus live and even save some money out of the small honorarium I was able to give them.

They were all very successful in their research work. They had

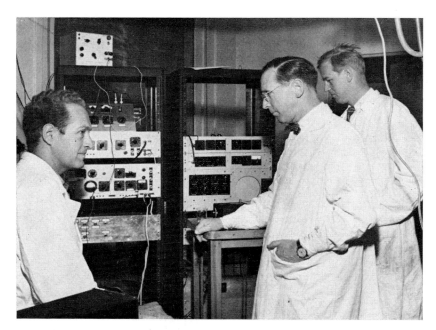

Dr. Melvin Cohen and Dr. Sven Landgren working with the author on the cortical reception of sensory messages.

previously only worked on cold blooded animals, frogs, toads or fishes. In Stockholm they became familiar with mammalian physiology which involves quite a different technique. They all of them did very well after their return to Japan; Susumo Hagiwara went to California where he discovered new sensory organs in fishes. I owe them all (and their teachers who trusted me enough to send their best pupils to me in Stockholm) my deepest and heartfelt gratitude.

Between Eric Neil's visits Dr. Melvin Cohen from Eugene, Washington State, worked with me and Sven Landgren on our experiments in peripheral as well as central parts of the nervous system, using monkeys and cats. Sven Landgren had just returned from a year's visit to Sir John Eccles's laboratory at Canberra, Australia, where he had taken an active part in Eccles's discovery of the inhibitory post – synaptic potential, (I.P.S.P.). He had thus acquired a great familiarity in using microelectrodes for recording extra-and intracellularly from single nerve cell bodies. So we started with Cohen a rather extensive study of the reception of sensory signals in the tongue's sensory area of the cerebral cortex of the cat, hoping to be able to find out how impulses originating from the taste buds were received. We had very little success with this. In about fifty experiments we found only five cortical cells responding to the arrival of taste impulses, and I once again faced a dilemma: do the taste nerves project to another area of the cortex or are their receiving cells in the tongue's sensory area of the cortex too small for our electrodes? Ablation of this area in animals has not given a definite answer and the question is still open, as nobody has as yet found any other area. But in spite of our failure with taste, our experiments on the cortex gave us a host of valuable information about the arrival, reception and further cortical effects of other sensory stimuli to the tongue. We also discovered a new inhibitory phenomenon which we could prove took place within the cerebral cortex. We wrote this up in a rather extensive paper which has been much overlooked as it had to be published as a supplement to the *Acta Physiologica Scandinavica,* though I am proud to be its co-author. Most of the experimental work was done by Sven Landgren who also wrote the greatest part of the manuscript. Some of our theories and findings about the cortical reception of sensory signals were no doubt quite in advance of their time and it took some while to get them accepted by specialists in the U.S.A. Because of this Melvin Cohen sent the manuscript to one of my colleagues in the U.S.A. but without telling me until later. But this colleague could not (or did perhaps not want to) grasp some of our ideas, I suppose because they were not compatible with his own views. All this caused a year's delay in publication. A scientist's life is not always a bed of roses; he often has to fight fiercely to get his ideas accepted. It has always been so, and it will continue thus for ever. Life is a struggle and even Nobel laureates do not have an easy time. There are always some people who particularly enjoy trying to prove a famous man wrong in one or more details. Such criticism rarely leads to anything positive and I have always avoided lengthy polemics in the scientific journals, as in my experience they only result in bitterness. You should only argue face to face at meetings and symposia where you can both give and take, and such discussions are often very profitable, frequently leading to better friendships. Scientific debates should be held in the spirit of my beloved teacher Jöns Johanson who once said, in a much quoted speech at the closing of the International Congress of Physiology at Boston in 1929, "It is not the possession of truth but the searching after it which characterizes the cultured man."

CHAPTER XVIII

Visiting Professor at Berne. — A nocturnal arrest.

It was a wonderful privilege to be invited as Gastprofessor (visiting professor) to the University of Berne by Alexander von Muralt, Head of the famous Hallerian Institute of Physiology. He met me at the station and took me to Bären Hotel in the old part of the city. At night I was awakened by loud knocking on my door. I looked at my watch; it was 4 a.m. I jumped out of my bed, went to the door, and asked: "Who is there?" – "Just open the door," said a deep male voice. "Why should I open it?" I asked, "What do you want?" "Open it," said several voices, "it is the police". Well I had to obey, and in walked two heavyweights in plain clothes followed by a very distressed night porter. "Let me see your passport," said one of the fellows. "How do I know that you really *are* policemen?" I asked, "Please identify yourselves." So they presented their identification cards. I handed them my passport, issued by our Foreign Office. I had brought courier mail to the Swedish Embassy. They read my name: Gulle Yngve Zotterman, "*Gulle*[1] – that's not a name," said the man. "Well" I replied, "I can't help that." "You are no professor," he added. I tried to take it calmly and said' "What makes you think that?" "You are the international criminal Zotterman," snarled the big fellow. "What have I done?" I asked with great curiosity. "You have stolen pictures from our National Gallery," he replied. I tried to explain to them that I had arrived only last night at Kloten airport outside Zürich, and this was stamped in my passport, and that Professor von Muralt had introduced me to the hotel proprietor the evening before. They began to look at each other in some

[1] See also Part One for instances of the embarrassement sometimes caused one by my unusual first name.

201

confusion and after a long discussion in Switzer Deutsch, which I did not understand, they left my room without saying another word or looking at me.

Alex von Muralt and his charming wife Alice were, of course, most amused when told about this incident, but the old hotel proprietor looked very worried and said: "How terrible for you." "Oh never mind," I said. "But you do not realize the significance of this incident; there is a *Steckbrief,* a circular, in every police station in Switzerland; wherever you go you may be arrested." However, as I stayed in Berne during the whole of my sojourn I avoided any further complications.

I had a very good time in Berne; during my first visit there Alex von Muralt and I tested the effect of an anti-vitamin B1 on the nerve endings of the frog's tongue, and were able to finish our experiments in the month I was there. The following year I spent a month in the same lab working with Dr. Robert Stämpfli, a distinguished specialist on nervous conduction and a most charming companion. We managed in a short time to obtain further evidence for a saltatory conduction in myelinated nerve fibres working on the very slender cutaneous nerves in the dorsal lymph sac of the frog.

During that time I rented a furnished room from a French-speaking widow in the Kirchenfeld area on the south side of the river Aare which runs through the centre of the City. She was a very kind old lady, who gave me some practice in French each morning when she served me tea with fresh brioches and cherry jam for my breakfast.

All the embassies are situated in that part of the city. The Chancery of the Swedish Embassy was just around the corner and I often went there to read the Swedish newspapers. The cashier, Miss Aga Annerfalk, was a great help. She had, as a matter of fact, given me the address of my hostess; and she introduced me to many friends of hers who used to join her in the evening for

202

dinner in a small *pensione* near the bridge. We went to the theatre and opera and visited many excellent restaurants. Swiss cooking has all the virtues of the French and Italian culinary arts. I do not know any place where you can get a better *côte de veau* with creamed morchels than in Schuldheiss Stübl in Hotel Schweizerhof in Berne. The place is usually crowded with diplomats, who generally know the best places to eat.

In 1952 Ambassador Torsten Hammarström had moved into the Embassy. He was a skilful diplomat, a gracious host and a great lover of fine food and wine. He was a slim, elderly bachelor who knew Italy and France from many years of diplomatic service in Paris and in Rome. He brought beautiful brocade and silk textiles for the newly decorated Embassy in Thunerstrasse where he lived and entertained. The floors were covered with giant Chinese carpets about one inch thick which he managed to buy while he was in China. His dinners were delicious. A few days before giving them he drove to Dijon in France, bought his provisions and brought back with him one of their famous chefs. Some of his wines were gifts from the wine cellar of Baron Rothschild.

Once at his dinner table I was placed next to a small, fragile old lady from Berne. Trying to find some subject for conversation with my rather silent companion I ventured, "Have you and your family lived long in Berne?" "Yes," she replied very shortly, "for 1300 years." After the dinner I repeated this to my gracious host and he said, "Yes, that's right, one of her husband's ancestors is riding the horse in the equestrian statue in front of the cathedral. Both their families have lived here since the days of the Roman Empire." I learned later that this lady received many young girls from Germany and other European countries to finish their education and introduce them into Society.

When in 1955 Alex von Muralt served as Rector Magnificus of the University I had an invitation to go to Berne for the award of an honorary V.M.D. degree. At Kloten airport outside Zürich,

The Rector Magnificus of the University of Berne, Professor Alex von Muralt, delivers his graduation lecture. The honorary graduates seated are: Alan Hodkin, Yngve Zotterman and A. Bovery, 1955.

I met Dr. Alan Hodgkin and other colleagues who were also heading for Berne. It was a very happy reunion, so happy that I forgot my briefcase at the airport and my luggage in the train to Berne, and arrived carrying my friend's luggage before I discovered my loss. However, Switzerland is a very orderly country. Alex went to the telephone and a few hours later all my things arrived at his house, where I was sharing a double bedroom with Alan Hodgkin, the same guestroom in which Brita and I used to sleep.

The graduation ceremony started at 9 a.m. in the great Hall of the Casino north of the Kirchenfeld Bridge. Alex von Muralt presided in the centre of the platform, dressed in a magnificent robe with a high velvet beret; at his side he had the different deans of the other faculties. Among the *promovendi causa honoris* I saw Alan Hodgkin, with Dr. Bovery, the director of the giant electrical company Brown-Bovery, and a few others. In the background were students dressed in beautiful, colourful uniforms with the banners of their fraternities; and a huge academic orchestra.

Alex von Muralt gave a splendid lecture about nervous conduction, a historic review of the great advances in our knowledge during the last few decades. He is a most gifted speaker. Then he started the Graduation Act in Latin: *Quod bonum faustum* etc. We stepped forward one after the other, addressed in Latin by the dean in question, and received our diplomas in a beautiful scarlet red cylinder decorated with bears, which are the arms of Berne. It was a splendid ceremony, the big hall full of guests who applauded the speakers, the *promoti* and the music.

There was a fine meal served at 1 p.m. where I met again my dear friend Torsten Hammarström, who was among the honoured guests. I was asked to present the thanks of the *promoti* in an after-dinner speech in German. I made it quite short, ending up with a skål for further international organization, praising Switzerland's leading position in international co-operation.

The next day we had a nice supper in Muralt's lovely house, in Viereckerstrasse. In the afternoon Alan Hodgkin and I each gave a lecture in the Hallerian Institute. Alan gave a very good one, but mine was not very good, I was too tired, I believe, and I spoke in German which I should not have done. Alex thanked me from the chair, but afterwards he said: "It was a rather bad performance, I had expected better from you." Well, I was ashamed. But one has one's off days.

We were sitting in Muralt's house in the drawing room having coffee after dinner. Everybody was very tired and the conversation was flowing rather sporadically. I felt quite weary. Should I tell a good story? . . . but Alex is such an excellent raconteur. Finally, when everybody seemed to be half asleep, I started to tell my story about the Ethiopian Prince who was to arrive at the Paris airport for a peace conference. There was a large group of journalists

Yngve Zotterman receiving the diploma; behind him the
Dean of the Veterinary Faculty, Professor Stiegler.

from all over the world waiting for his arrival. It was delayed.
Then at the bar one of the journalists suggested," Should we not
direct a few common questions at the Prince?" They agreed and
after a while the plane arrived; the little prince alighted. The
correspondent of *The Times* stepped forward and said: "Your
Imperial Highness, will you kindly answer two questions for all
the ladies and gentlemen of the world press assembled here".
"With tsh... sh... greatest... shl... pleasure," replied the

Princee; "I am tsi... tsi... fully prepared to answer your questions, pri... tu, nib..." – "Our first question," said the old gentleman, quite undisturbed by this performance, "is whether you have received and studied all the items in advance in your country's capital?" "Pri... tsi... bang," said the Prince, "we have received... rrt... and studied all the items... psi... ti... rulsh,..." "Our second question is, your Imperial Highness" said *The Times* correspondent very calmly, "Have you been authorized by the Imperial Government to sign any eventual treaty?" "To your second question, pu... tri... bang," replied the Prince, "I can answer that... tri... tri... bang, brr... I have been fully authorised bang... ptsi... to sign any eventual treaty." Then a young lady from the *Daily Mail* could not resist it. She went up to the Prince and said, "Your Imperial Highness, would you kindly answer an extra question"? The little Prince looked very earnestly at her and said: "Pri... tch... I am quite willing to answer... bang... ptsi... your extra question, Madame". – "Have you been to England, or where did you learn to speak such wonderful English?" asked the girl. "My dear young lady – pse, psc, bang – Madame (whistle, whistle), I have never been to England – bang, pffc,.... I learnt my English (bang, whistle) from the Addis Abeba short-wave transmission station (whistle)... bang..."

I have told this story many times with great success but I have never seen anybody laugh so much and so long as Dr. Bovery and beautiful Ann-Marie Bovery, his elegant wife. They slapped their knees and, looking at each other, almost exploded with mirth. After quite some minutes of laughing, the pretty Ann-Marie Bovery recovered her powers of speech and smilingly said: "How did you know?" "How did I know what?" I asked, quite astonished: "Oh, didn't you realize, that the Emperor Haille Selassie of Ethiopia paid a visit to the Brown-Bovery factory in Baden a few months ago and that Dr. Bovery presented him with a short-wave transmitter as a farewell gift."

CHAPTER XIX

Our cottage at Ljusterö. — Hjalmar the Butcher.

When I returned from the U.S.A. in 1940, I felt depressed. Finland had been forced to accept very, very hard peace conditions; its future looked grave, and still worse was the fact that the Nazis had occupied Denmark and Norway. To add to my depression, the Chancellor of the University and the Government had not accepted the recommendation of three of my four referees that I should be appointed the chair of physiology at Uppsala University. The referees were all young, expert physiologists. One of them, Ragnar Granit, was to be a Nobel Prizewinner, the second, Einar Lundsgaard of Copenhagen, might very well have been given a Nobel Prize for his work in muscle physiology, and the third was Professor Georg Kahlson, distinguished physiologist and founder of a great school of physiology. His associates are now filling many of the chairs of physiology in Sweden. The fourth referee was a local man who never forgot that Brita's uncle had not placed him high enough in a previous competition. Then I was declared unsuitable for a chair at G.C.I., where I had taught physiology for 11 years. The papers passed through the Collegium of Professors of Karolinska Institutet where everybody but my old friend Professor Liljestrand, gave me their votes. The Board of G.C.I., where my colleague Abramson was the president, declared me incompetent. No wonder that I lay down on my sofa, saying, "I have been declared incompetent, I am not worth a cent." All the posts were taken by junior colleagues; my future looked very uncertain.

But I had a wise mother. In the new year she said, "You must find a country place, some small house somewhere for the family. The children need to spend their summer in the country." So I

The cottage at Ljusterö.

started to look around for a suitable place. At last found it on the
big island of Ljusterö at Marums Fjord only 3 miles from Hugo
Theorell's cottage.

We rowed over the narrow fjord to a small concrete jetty
where two small boats were tied up. A pillar on each side carried
a pot of red flowers; the road led up to a small wooden house
on two floors, yellow with white corners. A glass veranda faced
the fjord although an avenue of four linden trees on each side
hid most of it from view. The garden, mostly wild, was brilliant
with millions of primulas and small orchids in blossom – *Orchis
sambucina* (Adam and Eve as they are called in Sweden) with
scarlet or yellow flowers. It was irresistible. We bought it and
then spent a dozen happy summers there with our three children
and our many friends in the neighbourhood.

The house was originally built by a ship's timberman. It was
cheaply built, but a genuine country cottage. It was partly furnished

Helena at Ljusterö.

and in the first years we had no electricity and no oil for lamps, so, like everybody else, we had to rely on carbide lamps. Drinking water we took from a well drilled to 120 feet in the rock.

It was wonderful to be there with the children and our big Rottweiler dog, King. We swam and rowed and fished. Every day we discovered a new kind of flower in our border. Once Johan, aged 4 years, rushed in with a piece of black pudding in his small hand shouting very excitedly, "Mother, mother, there is black pudding growing in the garden."

After we had Margit and Hugo Theorell to dinner there for the first time, Theo asked for a saw and started to fell four of the linden trees which hid our view over the fjord. The following day I got some help to take them all away. In the war years of 1941-5, we had to take the steamer *Saxaren* out to a jetty about half a mile from our cottage. It took two or three hours but we met many friends on board and it was a lovely journey through the beautiful fjords to Linanäs where we often took the bus, in those days driven by gas from a wooden or charcoal furnace at the back. Sometimes we had to get out when the engine was not able to climb a hill.

In the garden we had strawberries and on May 25., St. Urban's day, I put beans in the ground, but not before because of the night frosts. It was my special interest and duty to keep the land free from weeds and pick berries and beans. We made quite a lot of jam for the winter and I often sterilized about forty glass quart-jars of *haricots verts,* which we took back to town with us.

As I spent a good deal of my summer with the Navy, Brita was helped by an old fisherman and butcher, Hjalmar Anderson, and his small wife Victoria, who had a cottage across the Marum fjord. He was a jack-of-all-trades; a lumberjack, a fisherman, a farmer and slaughterer, etc., and a fine singer. He was a tall, somewhat bent fellow, with a big nose, long legs and arms and two very lively brown eyes in his long, furrowed face. Butcher Hjalmar was the nickname by which he was known everywhere. He crossed the big island with his horse-driven cart selling pork and other meat; the horse had often to find his way home by himself, as Hjalmar, after singing happily, went off to sleep.

He was a very great help to us. In the spring and late autumn weekends he went to our cottage and lit a fire, rowed the boat to the jetty when we arrived with the steamer, and helped us in many ways.

His little wife Victoria had a very happy disposition: she was always smiling. She used to come and help Brita clean the house

Hjalmar the butcher.

and bake the coffee bread, so much loved by the children. They were seldom both with us together. In a way we preferred this. Hjalmar was always very anxious to have a *Kaffehalva,* i.e. half coffee and half aquavit.

Sitting there in our small kitchen drinking this coffee, he told us very dramatic stories of his life. He believed in black magic, and would describe how he, as a boy, rowed all the way to Stockholm (24 nautical miles) to sell fish and sour milk. He had a good baritone voice and knew a lot of old songs. "I should of course have gone into opera," he said once. And I am quite sure he was right. He still sang very well in his late sixties. Our children listened open-mouthed to stories of his hunting prowess. He once shot a sea hawk which was flying with a big pike in his talons. When he cleaned the pike he found a golden ring inside her. When the children uttered some doubts as to the truth of his stories, he would cross himself and swear it was all true. He was very

Agneta and Johan in the small motor boat.

entertaining indeed, and we all loved Hjalmar. But sometimes, when he was the worse for liquor, he would be difficult and was very unpleasant to his family. At the beginning of an alcoholic bout he used to sit drinking on a rock, at the edge of the forest, singing melodiously. Aha, said everybody, Hjalmar has got hold of some liquor. But later on in the day he often threatened his wife and children with his butcher's knives, and they had to hide themselves in the woods. Our little son Johan had obviously heard of this, because once when we had paid them a visit and were leaving their cottage, Johan, aged six, turned round in the doorway and said: "Farewell and God's Peace to this house." Everybody smiled but Hjalmar, who looked as if he had heard nothing.

One summer night I was woken up by Victoria who had run up our stairs and was knocking at our bedroom door on the first floor. "Please come at once," she cried. "Hjalmar is bringing up pints of blood." We rushed over in my outboarder and I found Hjalmar in

Helena.

his bed and looking very pale. He certainly had bled quite profusely – fresh, red blood. The diagnosis was clear: he was bleeding from burst varices in his oesophagus. He had complained to me previously that he felt something was wrong with his liver. He felt tired, and he feared he would die like his father from cancer of the liver. I managed to get him to the county hospital where he stayed a few weeks, returning after the bleeding had stopped. His strength diminished and next spring I had to send him to hospital again. He had the same disease as his father. I visited him several times, the last time a few days before he died. He told me that he would die soon. "I am fully prepared," he said. "I have made my debit and credit with Our Lord, I am not afraid." He was quite feeble, but suddenly he said, "Professor, how I

214

regret ..." "Don't think about it, Hjalmar," I said, "it is all forgotten." I thought he was sorry about chasing his wife with knives. He shook his head and said, "Oh no, I was thinking about the old days when the finest French Cognac cost no more than 1.75 (50 cents) on the steamer at Marum ... that one did not drink oneself to death."

A week afterwards we went to his funeral in Ljusterö's old wooden church, Brita and I in black. There were quite a few people besides his widow, their three daughters and their son, and their children, who followed his coffin when it was carried out to the open grave. When the coffin had been set down and the rector had read a last prayer, I stepped forward to the open grave, took off my doctor's hat, and read a poem of Heidenstam and bade farewell to our dear old friend Hjalmar. I had promised him I would do this.

Victoria had a huge funeral dinner in her house afterwards. She served several courses, as is the custom, and even a glass of Madeira wine. A few years later we went to her funeral. We missed them both enormously. The life on Ljusterö had lost one of its greatest charms – an intimate friendship with a local family. Our children went abroad in the summer to learn German, French and English. We rented out our cottage for a few summers and in 1955 we returned for the summer with Helena and her first baby from America. It was a fine summer, our last on Ljusterö. Next year we sold the house.

Road Safety Research. — Fille Fellenius.

When the Government finally decided in 1949 that it was necessary for research into the growing incidence of road accidents, the Road Safety Research Council was set up. It was presided over by the former President of the Trade Union Council, August Lindberg, who was a very popular man. Among the members were representatives of the Government's Road Board, headed by its General Director; a medical practitioner; a psychologist Valdemar Fellenius; some civil engineers and a statistician. As head of its office it had a civil servant from the Ministry of Transport, Mr. Hans Hansson. In 1955 after the death of the medical officer I was asked to join the Council.

I met there a group of talented and industrious men who – in their spare time – did their best to find and develop methods of approach for studying different aspects of our important but very difficult work. We had to throw light onto the causes of road accidents and try to find means of preventing them. The statisticians within the Council and those outside whom we employed brought us a great deal of important information. The technicians investigated the technical factors in accidents, like road surface, brakes and tyres, etc., and psychologists and medical people were brought onto the Council to study the human factors.

It was, of course, natural that the surgeons, who received and had to treat the casualties, should alert the authorities and demand that the automobile industry should spend more money to increase the safety of cars. The Council called leading authorities and scientists to public debates and scientific symposia. All this took a long time. At one of the first symposia (in 1962) I urged the industry to invest more money in the internal safety of the car than on developing its horse power. They laughed at me. "More safety or safety belts do not help to sell cars." That was only seven years ago. Today, after all that has happened, and after the great alarm caused by the young lawyer Ralph Nader in the U.S.A, who wrote the book *Unsafe at Any Speed,* their attitude is quite changed, although a faster motor still sells better.

Road safety research was a new applied science. We had no earlier forms or methods to follow. It was thus no wonder that it took a long time to develop. A few mistakes were made, some projects were not followed up or led nowhere. Gradually the Council managed to place research projects into the hands of competent people who were able to pursue and collect valuable information. This applied particularly to the projects concerned with automobile lighting and the recognition of road signs carried out at the Department of Psychology in Uppsala by Professor Gunnar Johansson and his associates. The medical aspects, the construction of the safety belts, etc., came finally into the capable hands of Dr. Bertil Aldman, a surgeon who now works fulltime for the Council, directing a medical safety research institute of the Road Safety Research Council. Gradually other well-trained and efficient young men could be brought in to hold full-time jobs. There is no doubt that the money which the Government supplied has been a very good investment. Better roads and better cars are bound to exert a great influence on road safety, but the main factor is human behaviour and it is in this field we have to concentrate in order to diminish the present mass killing on our roads.

The meetings of the Council were sometimes quite lively. The debate was very frank, at least for those of us who were free academic citizens. The members representing public administration had often to be convinced of the necessity of solving basic scientific problems before we could attack practical problems. I often had to fight very fiercely – sometimes in vain – but generally we agreed upon most projects and sometimes the "practical men"

217

grew more enthusiastic than we were about a project which they had at first rejected. This happened, for example, with the project for city planning applied for by Professor Sune Lindström, the architect of the Wenner-Gren Center, where the Council has its offices. It took a very long time, more than a year to persuade them. Generally most decisions were unanimous, but I nevertheless sometimes had a few reservations about them. I am more in favour of speed limits than are the administrators and the head of the State Police.

Our first President, August Lindberg, was succeeded by Axel Strand, his successor on the Trade Union Council. Strand, a Speaker of *Riksdagen,* was an extraordinarily skilful chairman; his great experience and intelligence was very valuable indeed. He was nearly perfect; you cannot say more, because perfection is impossible. We very much enjoyed his humour and the anecdotes of his long political life.

At one of our dinners he once told us that some of his political friends asked him if he did not feel nervous at presiding over a council consisting of a great number of scientists. "Well," he replied, "haven't you read Mark Twain? He tells about a man who said it was very easy to catch rabbits." "Oh, no, that is very hard," said somebody else. "No, it isn't," said the man, "you just place yourself early in the morning in a cabbage patch and look like a cabbage. Then when the rabbits come for their early breakfast you can catch as many as you like."

I enjoyed my 15 years with the Road Safety Council, the last eight as its vice president because I lived so close to its office and was easily accessible for signing reports and bank orders. I just had a rather nagging feeling that I should take a more active part in safety research; but I had quite a few young research workers from all over the world assisting me in my own work on sensory organs, so I had to stay with my basic physiological research.

One summer, in the mid-thirties, our submarine flotilla was on manoeuvres in the Saxar Fjord, north of Stockholm, with a voluntary corps of civil motorboats swarming round our flagship H.M.S. *Svea* like bees round a queen. One day the Commodore, Count Gustaf Hamilton, said: "Zotterman, I don't know how to keep these chaps occupied." I answered "My father-in-law lives about ten miles from here; I could pay the old man a professional visit." "An excellent idea," he said, and told his aide-de-camp to get one of the motorboats to the gangway.

So, with my little black bag in my left hand, I saluted the flag from the gangplank with my right and stepped into a tiny speedboat piloted by a young man who, 20 minutes later, landed me (rather shaken) at the jetty outside Brita's father's house. My father-in-law was surprised at being visited by a naval commander until he realized who it was. After a time I returned to the speedboat and the rather bored young sublieutenant. And that was how I first met Valdemar Fellenius, a licentiate in literature who switched to psychology and became what we called a *Kändis,* which, literally translated, means a *known one.* He was a tall, handsome fellow, with a great shock of tawny hair, blue eyes and a noble bone structure, with the physique of a Greek god. His large hands always showed signs of his passion for engines, both at sea and on land. He was never happier than when he was behind a steering wheel.

The next time we met was at a public discussion on road accidents in the great hall of the Concert House in Stockholm. In the discussion which followed my lecture on industrial fatigue, Fellenius stepped onto the platform and gave a very interesting report on an investigation he had made on 'bus drivers in Stockholm, showing that about 5 per cent of the drivers were "accident prone" and were responsible for 75 per cent of all accidents. Fellenius was then an assistant to Professor David Katz, a German psychologist who had escaped Hitler and reached Sweden via England. He applied for, and was appointed to, a new chair of psychology,

Valdemar Fellenius.

paid for out of Eneroth's donation. Through Fellenius and his attractive wife Judith Lucia, who kept open house in the western garden city of Stockholm, we met Professor Katz and his wife Dr. Rosa Katz, a school psychologist.

David Katz, who then was in his fifties, could speak fairly fluent Swedish. He was keen to form a Psychological Society and he worked hard in his poorly equipped laboratory in a rather dilapidated apartment in an old house in Stockholm heated by log fires in large porcelain stoves. Katz managed in spite of the difficulties to create a much respected school of experimental psychology. He was very knowledgeable and experienced in the physiology of the old German school, and it was amazing to see what apparatus he built with such slender resources. Fellenius, who was skilful with his hands, helped him a lot in those days. They borrowed from my lab a Hipp's chronoscope which could record reaction times with an accuracy of 1/100 second. For many years we had a great mutual exchange of ideas and results, particularly after the meetings of the Psychological Society, when quite a few very interesting young men and women who worked with Katz would have supper together and continue the discussions over a meal.

Valdemar Fellenius's head was always full of ideas and he started a new research project at least once a month. If he had only brought a tenth of them to fruition, he would have been a great man. But after a few preliminary experiments he got some new idea to follow up, and went off at a tangent. It was a great pity, as he had all the qualities of a good experimental scientist; imagination, intelligence and dexterity.

When World War II started he soon got bored spending his time in a motor boat waiting for orders. His sister Hellis was married to a Cambridge don, Peter Tennant, Lecturer in Scandinavian languages – he speaks Swedish without any accent. They came back to Stockholm when Tennant was appointed attaché at the British Embassy. Tennant and Fellenius must have spoken together about submarine warfare, but wherever he got the idea from "Fille" (as we called him) managed to arouse the interest of the Swedish admiralty in a very special project. It was of course kept very secret, but once he invited me to his station on an island in the archipelago. There he was training young seals to find submarines on the sea-bed. They were beautiful animals, playful and always eager to dive after fish.

Imitations of submarine towers, the most vulnerable part of a submarine, were sunk at various places, with a bunch of fresh herrings attached to the tower-device. The willing grey seals who were always very hungry quickly found these targets. They could dive down to 40 fathoms. The next problem was to find the best method for them to carry explosives to destroy the submarine.

A professor of veterinary surgery helped Fille to shave bald patches on the fur of the animals so that a bomb could be attached. Engineers then helped to work out a magnetic device so that the bomb, with its delayed fuse, was released and fastened onto the submarine tower.

It took some time. Fille had to go out on audacious expeditions in March and April to catch new-born seals on the ice in the Bothnian Gulf using light aeroplanes which could land on the ice. He brought home a lot of these beautiful young animals still in their "white coats", a creamy fur. They had to be fed on very rich milk, but a few died and Mrs. Fellenius still wears a fur coat made out of these baby seal skins.

When Fille had got the project to work well, the admirals and the minister of defence came out on an inspection. The seals went out with their load, came back before the explosions, and everything worked perfectly. The admirals looked very happy. Only the minister, Mr. Per Edvin Sköld was unimpressed: "Tell me, Dr. Fellenius," he asked, "how do you train the seals to tell the difference between an enemy submarine and one of our own?" Fortunately the war soon ended and with it the imminent interest in submarine warfare.

Instead of concentrating on *one* research project for his doctor's degree, Fille became a member of the Road Safety Research Council of Sweden, for which he started quite a few projects and then founded a whole institute, The Psychophysical Institute of Stockholm's University. Its principal function was to devise psychophysical tests and interviews for vocational advice. There was a great need for this and Fille developed this institute quickly, recruiting personnel who had been trained in England. The Institute also did a lot of practical psychological research for different industries, schools and Government institutions. It grew steadily, in spite of very little financial aid from the Government. How Fille, leading a very irregular life, could administer this growing institute was a mystery to me, but he did so. Of course the president and the members of the board of the institute sometimes had to wait for half an hour, when Fille had kept one or two secretaries working all night to present his reports.

His institute grew as more and more investigations in applied psychology were requested from industry, schools and colleges. Fille devised entrance examinations for the Polytechnical High School, as well as for students entering medical faculties, where only a limited number cf students were admitted each term. This last project was requested by a Government Committee, which had as members, Prof. Katz, a representative of the medical teachers, Dr. Rexed, a representative of the medical students (who is now Dr. Ulf Nilsonne), *a member of the Riksdag* and a member of the board of schools.[1]

At that time, as at present, a student who wanted to enrol in medical school had to send in his application to the office of the Chancellor of the Swedish Universities. There his total marks in science examinations were calculated and the best students (probably about 180), were admitted to our three medical schools. Those left could enter universities to study, for example, statistics, biology, genetics, etc., for a B. A. degree; every examination giving them cumulative marks for later admission to medical school. There are some, however, for whom the medical profession is a vocation. I had several classmates in this category, who went as medical missionaries. One of the bravest, Theodor Ollén, died in a tent on the highland steppes of Mongolia. These young men and women were not always among the brightest at high school and had to spend anything from one to three years collecting marks to enter the medical faculty, a great waste of time and money which it would take them many years to repay. Eighty per cent of Swedish university students used to live on loans from banks.

-----

[1] I was acting as chairman.

Our Committee recommended that two-thirds of the students admitted for medical studies should be accepted after their primary student examinations, while the last third should be chosen after testing and interviewing. We had no reservations about this: our aim was that students who did not do particularly well at school (quite a few subsequently famous doctors and professors were not admitted straight away because of low marks) should be given the opportunity of immediate entry, without wasting time and money gaining additional marks. I thought our unanimous report would be accepted by the Government, but it was not, and the reason that it was not is quite a story.

At that particular time the biggest morning paper in Sweden, *Dagens Nyheter*, had a new editor, Herbert Tingsten, a professor of social science, a very forceful writer and speaker, and a fighter for liberal principles. The paper started a campaign to ridicule our psychophysical methods. Whether the editor or some of the young staff reporters were responsible is irrelevant. A young woman reporter went to the Psychophysical Institute under false pretences and undertook tests. She then wrote a very witty, satirical series of articles in *Dagens Nyheter* supported by an editorial by the chief editor. Worse still, the campaign spread to the biggest weekly magazine, the *Veckojournalen,* which carried similar articles. I was away in the Navy and poor young Fille had a tough time defending his institute and his profession. There were, of course, a few grains of truth in some of the criticism, but it was grossly overdone. What happened to our recommendations? The report was circulated in the medical faculties and the students' associations and failed to get its recommendations accepted. Why not? Neither Dr. Rexed who had now succeeded me as medical correspondent in *Dagens Nyheter* nor any of the representatives for the different categories in our Committee would defend the recommendations of the report which they all had signed; I was with the Navy. It was all very typical of Tingsten – he was brilliant and amusing in debate, but, as his successor as chief editor once wrote, the result of his criticism was always negative. "He does not hesitate to bring things down for the fun of the battle, but he has never built anything up."

So the medical schools of Sweden left it to the high school teachers to decide who should study medicine. I do not doubt that students who are brilliant in their last year at high school will do very well, but I am also convinced that the medical profession needs people for whom medicine is a vocation. Such people are not always found among the few in the high schools who have sufficient marks to be admitted to medical studies.

There was another great mistake made in those days by the leaders of the medical association of Sweden. In the 1920s a newly qualified doctor often had to serve for very little money or no pay at all for months, or even years, in a county hospital before getting a post as a district practitioner. Thus the Association recommended a limited admission to the medical classes. The result was that now Sweden has a scarcity of qualified medical practitioners. We have had to import doctors from Denmark, Norway, Yugoslavia, Austria, Greece, etc. You very rarely find any Swedish-born medical practitioner in the extreme north and in one big mental hospital you will find half a dozen foreign doctors with one Swedish psychiatrist in charge. It has been a grave miscalculation, but of course in a way Sweden has gained: we have now more than one thousand doctors in Sweden whose education has cost us almost nothing. The capital invested in a medical man at the age of 40 is about half a million Crowns ($100,000). In addition we need more people in our vast country. In the last few years the Government has, however, started new medical schools first in Gothenburg, then at Umeå in the north and at Linköping, and has increased the intake of the old schools, thus doubling the number of students admitted. They had to: the University Teacher's Union (U.L.F.) had long before warned the Government that they must prepare the universities for the rapidly growing number of students coming from the high schools. The Government's own calculations were proved to be far too low. We were not alone in criticizing and were supported by Dr. Richard Sterner, a prominent member of the Government's own Social Democratic Party and a former State Secretary. Well, it is easy to criticize a Government for what they have not done and I will gladly give credit here to the preceding Government which has done much for higher education in Sweden, more than any Government since the days of Gustaf II Adolf in the seventeenth century. So here I pay my respects to what the Government achieved during the 22 years of Mr. Erlander's leadership. I do not believe, looking back on what liberal and conservative Governments did earlier, that any other political party in power would have done better.

Let us now return to our friend Fille. He was shaken by all these events, but he always came up smiling. He started more new projects and the routine work of the Institute increased, giving it more income. But Fille needed a degree in order to advance in a university career and while his Institute flourished and grew in size, Fille's life became gradually more disorganized. He was unable to concentrate for more than a few days. His close friends tried to get him to go somewhere quiet to write his dissertation; he had a lot of quite good material. Instead he wanted to go to a skiing resort in the north. I protested, I even went to the President of the University, and we both agreed that he should not be allowed to go to such a lively place. But to no avail. Fille's great personal charm overcame the old President's objections. Fille pretended that he needed some distraction in the evenings when he had been writing all day. Well, he went skiing all day and had his distraction all night. He came back without having written a line.

But he was such an awfully nice fellow . . . we, his friends, often shook our heads but no one could resist his charm. How could you resist a man so full of often brilliant ideas; who could navigate,

226

even on the blackest of nights in the waters of the vast Stockholm Archipelago, who knew all those wonderful fishermen well enough to visit them and play jokes on them?

For many years Fille taught witness psychology to the police school in Stockholm and to the law schools at Uppsala and in Stockholm. He was often brought in to help the law courts when they had to question young children. The children often stayed a week or so in his house so that he could get to know them properly, in the hope that a taciturn child would open out and talk.

On one occasion a girl of 13 had been exposed to attempted rape, and the judge asked Fille to try and get this young girl to say who her assailant was. "Anna," asked Fille, "do you remember if he was tall or short?" No answer. "Can you tell if he had a beard?" Still no answer. "Do you remember how he was dressed?" The girl sat with lips shut tight, apparently quite disinterested. Finally Fille said: "But Anna, isn't there anything you can tell about the man?" The child suddenly looked up into his face and said, smiling: "He was like you, Sir."

The date for finishing his thesis for a Ph.D. degree was continually postponed until we finally accepted that we must abandon all hope for it. We tried everything we could to help him; a friend even offered to write the thesis if Fille would only supply him with the data and the arguments. Meanwhile the years passed. He had to have an operation for gastric ulcer, which partly was due to worry about his thesis and partly due to the irregularities of his way of life. He grew older. We began to grow somewhat worried on the board of his institute. We heard that he was often not there for days on end. Then one summer day, while in Capri, I heard that he had been drowned in the Stockholm Archipelago.

One night, with his little son, aged 8, by his second marriage and a young woman with her baby, he ran up against an underwater rock in the outer archipelago. He jumped into the sea to lift the boat off the rock. What happened then, whether his heart suddenly failed or his strength gave out, we shall never know; he disappeared in the dark night; his body was never found. The little boy, however, managed to get the boat afloat and began to search for his father. He had to give up, and took the boat in to the main island of Nassa where the survivors spent all night in a little cabin, the brave little lad making a fire and looking after the young woman, who was quite hysterical, and her baby son.

Fille had left us but his institute survived and has now developed into an indispensable institute for the practical training of psychologists. Even some of Fille's research projects were salvaged and published by his successors. Most people suspected that the finances of his institute were precarious. They were not. Fille's last year of administration resulted in a rather good surplus, more than was necessary to cover a few extra expenses for which he was personally responsible. We could even pay for a fine piece of ceramic art wich now is placed on a wall in the institute as a memorial to its founder, the irresistible Valdemar Fellenius, who was kinder to his friends than to himself.

CHAPTER XXI

The Professors form a trade union. — A Harpsund meeting.

The University professor's social status has always been high in Sweden. In the Royal Court *protocol* a professor had the rank of an army captain or a naval commander, although his salary was rather higher.

After the war prices rose considerably and we found it difficult to live on my new income. The interns in the hospitals complained and demanded wages which in 1945 were higher than the professor's salary. Their union invited Mr. Tage Erlander, at that time Minister of Education, to a dinner and discussed the matter with him. Erlander was very understanding, but added, "It will be difficult to give you a higher salary than the professors". "Oh," they answered, "their salary is ridiculously low." That gave me the idea of talking to my friend Richard Sterner who in 1946 was Myrdal's Secretary of State in the new Government. "You must form a union," he said; "and you must educate public opinion to realize that professors are underpaid. You must start by writing to the daily papers, etc."

So in 1946, I talked to my senior colleagues Professors Liljestrand and Hammarsten, as well as Hugo Theorell. They were all in favour of forming a union. We approached the Uppsala professors but there was no response from them. Arne Tiselius, for example, was in fact directly negative at that time, asserting that "Professors cannot form a trade union."

The following year, however, I obtained great support from the preclinical professors at Karolinska Institutet and I sent round a circular calling a meeting in Stockholm in the spring of 1947. Quite a few professors from Uppsala also turned up and we had a very lengthy discussion. Finally it ended in our forming a kind of interim board, with the young Professor Knut Rodhe of the Commercial

College as chairman *pro tempore* and me as secretary. Another meeting followed with lengthy discussions but very little decision, as the Uppsala professors were rather hesitant. They put forward all kinds of scruples.

One day in July 1947 Knut Rodhe and his wife came in their small sailing yacht to our cottage on Ljusterö. Sitting there on a rock, we suddenly decided to constitute our union and call it Sveriges Professorers Förening (the Swedish Professors Association). The interim board was then Knut Rodhe, chairman, Professor Gunnar Gunnarsson, vice chairman, and then ten members from the different universities. The Board elected me as secretary.

The first important activity was to contact the Government. Richard Sterner advised me to see the Secretary to Mr. Erlander, and ask him to suggest that we had an appointment with the Prime Minister and the ministers of agriculture and finance.

A few days later we were received in the Chancellory where we made our demands, asking for a committee to look into our economic conditions. Erlander was indeed very helpful and after a month the Government appointed a committee under the leadership of General Director Gustaf Stridsberg, a lawyer and our greatest expert on civil servant salaries. I had met him before at dinner parties at my cousin Albert Zotterman's, as Stridsberg was a member of the board of his mortgage bank. Stridsberg was the prototype of a Swedish higher civil servant, courageous, hard working, concise. He gave you the impression that he was very personally interested in your problems, listening carefully and asking knowledgeable questions.

His committee went round all the Swedish universities and university colleges, calling the professors to the meetings where they had an opportunity to discuss their problems.

On the committee was a young professor of law from Uppsala. In our union we had decided to ask for equal salaries for all profes-

230

sors – the university professors were at that time paid a little more than those from the polytechnical and veterinary colleges. We became aware that in Uppsala, and in Lund, many professors, including the *Rector Magnificus* at Lund, were agitating for discrimination. Thus we called the young committee member from Uppsala to special meetings where we gave him our arguments in favour of equal salaries.

After 2 years the committee handed in its printed report to the Government recommending a very substantial rise in professors' salaries – equal to that of a secretary of state, which meant a rise in social ranking to that of a colonel or commodore of the navy.

It would be an understatement to say that we were very happy. But we also had cause to be very sad too. The night before the report was signed, General Director Gustaf Stridsberg had a stroke and died. I had a certain suspicion that his death might hamper the success of our negotiations, and I was right. In the Chancery, the office people apparently got alarmed. They said that Parliament would never pass a proposal to give the professors such a high salary. "It would be like appointing 500 new secretaries of state," they said. Unfortunately such talk began to have some effect, as I learned from different sources. Some old university professors called on the Government to suggest that only university professors should be given the higher salary. Apparently their propaganda was successful, as far as I could learn from Mr. Weine, Minister of Education.

Then something rather unexpected happened. The Social Democratic Government decided to take in a few members of the farmers' party in order to secure a majority in the Riksdagen. I saw our opportunity. I rang up the state secretary in the Department of Agriculture and asked him where the new minister of education (a farmer) had obtained his higher education. He told me that he had graduated at the Alnarp Agricultural College outside Lund. Well, tell him then to support the demands of his old teachers, I said. So I asked for a meeting with the Prime Minister and the new minister of education, agriculture and finance, and we met them and then I pleaded very strongly that we should all receive the same salary. The new farmer ministers agreed, but the finance minister said nothing. I heard afterwards that the Social Democratic Government had previously made up their mind to give only the university professors the higher salary, but at their first meeting with their farmer colleague they did not want to fight them on a matter of not very great political importance. This was quite right. There is no reason to discriminate between professors in Sweden, as they all have very much the same background of years of higher education and research work. Many of our university professors have had their scientific training from professors at our polytechnical colleges and today even veterinarians have been appointed professors at the medical faculties of our universities.

The Government did not give us the salary which the Committee had proposed, but one approaching it. We fought very fiercely for Stridsberg's original proposition with the new minister of salaries, but in vain. At last S.A.C.O., the large organization which we had joined – very much against my will – advised us to give up. I never gave up, but our new chairman, Professor Gunnarsson, did. The negotiators from the Government threatened us that if the salaries were granted professors would not be allowed to have extra incomes. This was an empty threat because nearly every civil servant in the Chancery, including the General Directors with their relatively high salaries, had extra jobs for which they were paid.

We had a short time previously been joined as a separate association to the S.A.C.O., (Sveriges Akademiska Central Organisation) which included nearly all the University educated people, medical, dental, veterinary, lawyers, civil engineers, etc. It was our chairman, Professor Knut Rodhe, who had first been active

232

in forming the lawyers' association with the S.A.C.O., who was especially keen on it and who finally, very much against my will, managed to persuade the board of our professors' union to join. The S.A.C.O. officials, well paid "ombudsmen", were very anxious that we should accept the salary minister's offer – which was one degree lower than what the committee had suggested. The S.A.C.O. people tried every means in their power to persuade us – they said that they had been so insistent previously that they now had a bad reputation. I insisted and asked the Civil Minister to refer the matter back to the Government – all in vain. At that time we had a real chance which was only to return once more, and on that occasion S.A.C.O. again destroyed it. But I have to leave that now.

What we received in 1952 was, however, a very substantial step forward. The professors were all put in the same rung of the salary ladder as higher civil servants, with a salary equal to that of army colonel or commodore of the navy. There was also a very important change, or rather addition, to the statutes. Previously they stated that a professor had to give four lectures a week and examine his students. Now they added that it was a professor's duty to carry out research. This was important because it meant that research work was accepted as something equal to teaching.

The officials of S.A.C.O. soon found it troublesome to have to deal with a lot of small associations like our Professors' Union. They therefore suggested that all the university teachers, the assistants, the lecturers, the readers, etc., who had their own small unions should amalgamate. I understood their arguments and agreed to help them to achieve this and so in 1961 Universitets-lärarförbundet U.L.F. (University Teachers Federation) was founded and I was elected chairman of its board. We now became a body of 1200 members. We needed an office with a competent ombudsman. We raised the annual fee, which originally was 10 Crowns ($2). (It is today 400 Crowns [$80].) But the professors' salary today (1969) is 74,000 Crowns a year. It was only 18,000 Crowns in 1947.

We were very happy to find a young lawyer, Stig Persson, on the Council of Stockholm City. He proved very efficient and we were quite happy except for constant fights with the S.A.C.O. directors who were not very interested in our union. They listened instead to the big unions, like the high school teachers who numbered 15,000 members. We had constant arguments with the S.A.C.O. – always in vain. The elected chairman of the board – a public prosecutor in Stockholm – was particularly prejudiced against us: he hated his old teachers at the Stockholm Law School and thus all professors collectively. (So he told me once.)

We had also great difficulties with the young representatives of the amanuenses and assistants – the non-graduate members of U.L.F. They were young and arrogant, like left wing students today. They did not respect majority decisions. When their suggestions were not accepted by the others, they threatened to leave the Union and finally the situation became so inflamed that we had to part from them. They had their own headquarters at Lund University and were quite successful in their activities.

After a few years they succeeded in aquiring very substantial rises in salaries. They also managed to put one of their members on the board of S.A.C.O., where he constantly took part against the graduate university teachers.

In some ways it was an interesting time for me. I met a lot of fine colleagues from our different universities and colleges, and also quite a few members of our Government.

In 1947 Ernst Wigforss was Minister of Finance. He was a Ph.D., a former high school lecturer (lektor) and an ardent pioneer of Swedish Social Democracy. I remember that he found it "irrelevant" to raise the salary of a professor of pump technology. But when we told him that this professor in the polytechnical college had a Ph.D. degree and that his research field should be

234

called hydrodynamics, he gave in. But he was very unwilling to raise the salary of professors of surgery who earned so much from private practices. Well, I had to tell him that these professors, through his own wisdom, were exposed to very prohibitive marginal taxes so that 80% of their income was paid in income tax. Then he rubbed his hands and, looking very satisfied, said "Oh yes, of course, I had forgotten, we have already attended to that."

In those years there were so many changes in the Government that the new chairman Professor Gunnar Gunnarson and I had very often to call upon the ministers of finance, education, salaries and agriculture, as well as the party leaders in Riksdagen. In general we found them understanding. It is a fact that the development of the higher teaching has been very rapid during the long reign (23 years) of the former Prime Minister, Tage Erlander. The university teachers have all reason to be grateful to him, although the professors have not obtained the relative high salary position they once were offered by the Royal Committee. But that is to a certain extent their own fault. In 1965 they were offered it, but would not accept because the Government asked for additional lectures. I had then resigned, but tried to persuade my successor to agree. He feared that his acceptance would destroy the Professors' Union. I told him, "No fear, even if they protest now, they will be grateful within a few years." I am confident that today at least the majority of the professors would gladly accept a few additional lectures a year for a rise of 3,500 Crowns. But instead the professors joined the high school teachers and went on strike – which they lost to their great cost. Their refusal to accept those additional lectures have cost them very dearly. I made a rough estimation that the professors' Corps of Sweden (about 800) will in 10 years lose about 45 million Crowns. The political situation today is such that any rise in state salaries of the higher officials is absolutely out of the question. The political slogan of today in the Social Democratic Party, who now[1] has the majority in Riksdagen, is *equality*.

After World War II the number of students entering our universities increased almost in geometric progression. In the Department of Education they had made some kind of prognosis for the 1960s but every year the number of students entering was far greater than estimated. This was very alarming as the Government had made its plans based on wrong calculations. So we repeatedly called upon the Government for adequate measures to meet the actual situation, and to give the minister, Dr. Edenman, support when he was fighting the Minister of Finance, Mr. Sträng. A minister must not only have good ideas, he must also have a strong case when it comes to the final discussion about the budget. Then he must be able to extract what he needs from the Finance Department.

In the summer of 1962 the Prime Minister, Mr. Tage Erlander, invited a group of scientists from the universities and from industry to a meeting at his summer residence, Harpsund, in the province of Södermanland, about 2 hours' drive south of Stockholm. The theme was *Scientific Research and Society*. As soon as I got my personal invitation, I realized this was a chance for proper discussion with the leading men of our Government. So I called the members of the board of U.L.F. to a meeting, where we thoroughly prepared our programme and demands. We were, of course, anxious to have the advice of S.A.C.O. and called their young but very active and ambitious ombudsman, Bertil Östergren, to our preparatory meeting. However, he did not turn up. We called him on the telephone but his secretary told us he was engaged in more important matters. Our vice president called on him. No, he had no time. Obviously he created obstructions because he was hurt at not being invited himself. I tried to make him understand that I, like the others, was invited as an active research worker, not as the repre-

---

[1] 1969.

236

sentative of a professional association. He refused to come and place himself at our disposal. So we worked out a two-page programme and financial demand for me to hand over to the Prime Minister and the ministers concerned.

I arranged with the Prime Minister's personal adviser in scientific affairs, Professor Bror Rexed, M.D., to meet him at 7 a.m. when his train came into town from Saltsjöbaden. It was a fine sunny morning in early August 1962. We drove down through delightful scenery. In the car I told Rexed that I had a written *aide mémoire* from U.L.F. in which we made some demands on the Government. He was anxious to see it. After having read it twice he exclaimed: "This will be passed now." "What do you mean?" I asked. "Well," he said, "you know that some of these demands have been made recently by a small association of Social Democratic undergraduates under the leadership of Dr. Elvander. But when S.A.C.O. comes forward with these demands, it will be quite different. The Government will have to listen and do something." I did not tell him that S.A.C.O.'s leading official had refused to co-operate. After an hour's drive we turned into the narrow, winding roads which in another hour would lead us to Harpsund.

The Harpsund manor in the early nineteenth century style with wings is beautifully situated by a small lake. The whole estate was the property of a rich Stockholm merchant family, Wicander, who, among other things, had made a lot of money out of cork from Portugal. In 1952 C. A. Wicander donated the whole estate to the Government as a summer residence for the Prime Minister. This happened just at the time when Tage Erlander was head of the Government. So for seventeen summers the Erlander family spent their summer here, receiving numerous visitors like Kruschev, Harold Wilson and other political leaders and statesmen from all over the world. But Harpsund is also known for the conferences which Erlander arranged there for the members of the Government to meet industrial leaders, union leaders, scientists, writers, etc., for free and informal discussions.

The former Prime Minister of Sweden, Tage Erlander and Mrs. Aina Erlander outside their summer residence at Harpsund. (Photograph by permission of Keystone Press Agency, London.)

Bror Rexed and I arrived in good time for breakfast on the veranda. As it was a very fine and warm day, Erlander suggested that we should start our meeting outdoors in the garden and there, in the shade of two-century-old maple trees, we grouped together and started our discussion.

Young Dr. Elvander from Uppsala was a very keen debater. He and Professor Rexed were, of course, better prepared than most of the other scientists who apparently had not had time to look into the actual problems to be debated. They asked for more money for apparatus, or complained that they had no secretary or that every lab needed an instrument maker, etc. When I caught the Prime Minister's eye after an hour's discussion, I read our written resolution *in extenso*. It contained demands on six points:

(1) That the social security of the research-lecturers at the universities must be solved before 1 July 1963.

(2) That a special committee should be created immediately in order to investigate the education and professional career of the research workers.

(3) Radical reinforcement of the qualified teaching resources at the universities must be made starting in the budget year 1963–64 on the professors' and readers' level in the first instance.

(4) The possibilities of engaging retired professors for teaching as well as for research and investigation to improve teaching methods should be investigated.

(5) There should be essential increase of the Government's interest and economic allowances for research and higher education.

(6) A special expert organization should be appointed for a thorough investigation into the economic resources and their distribution and priority, with facilities for regular meetings with the Government.

At the luncheon afterwards on the veranda I happened to sit next to Gunnar Sträng who still is (1969) the Minister of Finance. "Yngve," he said, "I thought I was at a trade union meeting when I heard you read your resolution this morning." "I take that as a compliment," I said to the former leader of the farm workers' union.

I do not remember much of the ensuing discussion. Except

for Elvander and Rexed, the other scientists were rather unprepared, but it was obvious that the ministers present, Sträng, Edenman, Persson and young Mr. Palme, Erlander's private secretary, obtained sufficient information. Mrs. Erlander gave us a very good dinner and afterwards, with coffee and Cognac, the discussion went on indoors until midnight.

We came out into the beautiful bright Swedish summer night when the glow of the northern sky – the sun was only a few degrees under the horizon – was reflected in the still water of the lake in front of us. There at the small jetty the tiny rowing boat was moored, in which Erlander used to take out visiting statesmen for an absolutely private *tête à tête*. He did this with Kruschev and many others and so far, I believe, only Mr. Harold Wilson, the British Prime Minister and Labour Party leader, has refused this opportunity for an absolutely undisturbed conversation.

We had spent a very pleasant day with our young and cheerful Prime Minister. I chatted for some 10 minutes by the lake with Palme. Then I decided to drive home straight away as I did not feel I could sleep after such a full day. So I started my car and drove out on the narrow roads in the still night. I saw the reflexes from the keen eyes of a red fox close by in a ditch and further on I had to step on my brakes as a huge elk jumped across the road only 30 yards in front of me. It was rather frightening, but the elk – and I – came off unscathed. Finally at 3 o'clock in the morning I arrived at our apartment at Wenner-Gren Center and told my sleepy Brita what a day I had.

A few weeks later I signed a more detailed *aide mémoire* which we handed in to Dr. Edenman, the Minister of Education. Bror Rexed's pronouncement on that August morning proved to be true. The Government decided – after some time, of course – to create a special scientific council, headed by the Prime Minister, and a royal commission was elected for investigating and reforming the researchers' education and career prospects, etc. That committee

240

was terribly slow; it did not manage to report until 1966–67, after 4 years' work. Although the initiative for it came from U.L.F., not a single member was elected from those active within our Union. Instead they chose quite a few younger men whose experience of scientific research was next to nil. The result did not gain much approval among the universities and the Government bill of 1969 was very diluted. We hope that the new Government appointed in the autumn of 1969 will have more power to bring about the essential changes and improvements in higher teaching and in research conditions.

Nearly all of our demands (except one) have thus been met by the Government (although not to our full satisfaction). They have totally forgotten the retired professors. A university professor in Sweden may retire on 30 June after his sixty-fifth birthday, but he may remain in office for another year if he wishes. Then he receives a pension of about 65% of his former salary. Should the salary be raised he must have been in service 5 years afterwards in order to receive 65% of that rise. If he retires a year after the rise he receives only 20% of the 65% of the rise, etc., until, after 5 years in service, he receives the full 65% of the rise in salary. Thus there are still old, retired professors living who only receive half the pension which they pay me, who retired on 30 July 1965.

But what we demanded in 1962 was that retired professors who still were active and in good health should continue to be employed in research and in teaching. Nowadays, a professor at 66–70 is generally in quite good enough health to do a reasonable amount of teaching. It is a great shame that the authorities have not employed more of these numerous old professors for teaching. It is particularly wrong at a time when there is such a lack of qualified teachers at the higher level. There are now professors who are compelled to handle sixty graduate students. I managed to give a class in elementary neurophysiology for the freshmen studying psychology at Stockholm 4 years after my retirement, but this spring (1969) I was told that university reforms did not allow enough money for "such qualified teaching". So I was sacked. They paid me only 105 Crowns a lecture, including the examination. My teaching thus cost the Government, for eighty lectures a year plus the examination of 170 students, only 10,000 Crowns – one seventh of a professor's present salary.

At the Harpsund meeting I suggested to Mr. Sträng that a retired professor who is doing full-time teaching or research should be paid the difference between a professor's salary and his pension and he agreed. I tried for years to induce U.L.F. to plead for this, but the young people on U.L.F.'s board were not sufficiently interested. They will be one day, I fear.

CHAPTER XXII

The "Key War" strikes the Academy.

In the middle of the "key war" I was elected a member of the Royal Swedish Academy of Science. According to tradition, I dressed up for my first meeting in tails, decorations and white tie, with the arms of the Academy embroidered in black silk on each side of the black velvet collar of my tail coat. The President, the Permanent Secretary and the Notarius always appear in full evening dress and decorations, while the members turn up in ordinary clothes – except for their first appearance, when they are briefly addressed and welcomed by the President. The President in 1955 was the distinguished geologist Dr. Geijer, who had an unlimited store of anecdotes which he regularly told us after supper, when we had coffee, and Cognac or punsch, in the spacious antechambers of the assembly hall. The secretary was the very popular Arne Westgren, a physical chemist. His last years of office were certainly much disturbed by a most unusual event, the so-called "key war".

I will try to summarize this rather tragicomical affair. The somewhat belligerent Professor Rudolf Florin, a great botanist world-famous for his studies of Gymnosperms and also Director of the Bergian Botanical Garden near, and owned by, the Academy, sent a complaint to the Academy that his young colleague Professor Selling, head of the paleobotanic department of the National Historic Museum, at that time administered by the Academy, had refused to give him keys to the collections in the Museum. He wanted to go there at nights to pursue his studies of fossil trees. In central China a small group of a Sequioa had just been discovered which was only known from fossils and was not believed to exist any more. (I will not go into details.) It developed into a fierce fight. The legal adviser to the Academy brought in a barrister to examine the dispute. He advised the Academy to bring the case before the law courts. There were endless discussions at the Academy meetings, as some members took the part of the young paleobotanist, Selling. The lawyers succeeded, advised by psychiatrists, in getting Selling to undergo lengthy examinations in a mental hospital, but with no positive outcome. The whole proceeding was reported *in extenso* in the daily newspapers; the left wing and liberal press defended the accused; there was even an interpellation in the Riksdag. The court's decision I have forgotten; it was of no importance in itself as Selling was not imprisored he just had to pay a small fine by decision of the Court of Appeal. But the whole affair was utterly harmful to the Academy's reputation, and the Government made a substantial reduction in its usual annual subsidy. I was warned about this possibility early on by my friend Nils Aastrup, the leader of the liberal group of the first chamber of the Riksdag, but I was too new in the Academy to influence matters. It was a long and deplorable affair, and boring too, for it was most unedifying to listen to this quarrel, which delayed the usual lecture for hours. Normally the business agenda, in the capable hands of Arne Westgren, could be gone through in less than half an hour. After the lecture, which was always the last item of the programme, the members went to supper on the first floor, where a cold and warm buffet – the real old-fashioned *Smörgåsbord* – was served on the landing. After long meetings it was very pleasant to get a snapps and a beer and sit down among colleagues and friends. When supper was over, we went down for coffee and *avec* in the antechamber, where we sat around a great oval table. After a while the President arose to perform his duty of addressing the member who had given the lecture. There was, of course, an opportunity to let off steam – often these after-supper speeches were genuine jewels of wit and rhetoric, especially in 1967–9 when Hugo Theorell was the President.

There is a most cordial atmosphere at these suppers and their *Nachspiels*. Sometimes you can tell a story – but not too often! I once told the following story which I had from my old friend Ralph Gerard, a distinguished American physiologist. When the Ark was stranded on the mountain of Ararat, Noah let down the gangway and told all the various pairs of animals to go out and multiply. After a year Noah went on an inspection tour and found everything quite satisfactory. There were small lambs, kittens, calves, puppies, etc. But in one corner of the garden he found a very gloomy pair of snakes, all alone. "Didn't I tell you to go out and multiply?" demanded Noah. "Yes, you did," said the male snake, "but, Sir, how can we?". "Why not?" asked Noah. "You see, Sir, we are *adders*." Well, that *was* a problem and Noah went back to his Ark rather confounded. Some years later he came back to the same place and found the same pair of snakes happily surrounded by a lot of youngsters. "How lucky that you have succeeded," said Noah, "but how did you manage it?". "Oh," said the old male snake, "you see, Sir, we invented a log table, so now even adders can multiply!"

I have always considered this a good mathematical story which should be appreciated by scientists, but nobody smiled. I felt rather downcast, but then a friend patted me on the shoulder and whispered: "Don't worry; the old fellows speak and understand German and French quite well, but their English is very poor. They couldn't follow your excellent story."

All academies with a limited number of members suffer from the tendency of the average age of their members to increase. The Royal Engineering Academy of Sweden coped with this by transferring a member, when 65 years old, to a group of passive members. They retain their rights, but are not allowed to vote. In our Academy of Science a new member could be elected after the seventieth birthday of an existing member, who still retained his full membership. But the election of new members followed a very complicated system. It often took 3–5 years to fill the vacancy. Many members thus felt that it was important to work for some means of rejuvenating our Academy of Science. I had talked to Ragnar Granit about it several times and finally, when he was elected President in March 1962, he suggested that we should try to rejuvenate the Academy by changing the statutes. For a week in the beginning of August 1962 we went to the Granit family's summer resort out on the most western part of the Finnish archipelago at Korpo. There, in the fine summer weather, we drew up the lines for new statutes.

At the beginning we were both much in favour of a very radical change. We should have liked to do away with all the twelve classes and create an Academy more like that of the Royal Society in London. I had earlier received all the statutes and practical rules from Lord Adrian, who was President of the Royal Society from 1951 to 1956. Granit had just been made a foreign member. But we had to abandon such radical changes for practical reasons. It took a very long time, until 1967, before the new statutes were accepted by the Academy and later on legalized by the Government. The new statutes had previously been subjected to long debates and meetings of our Administerial Committee as well as of the Academy. Many good new rules were rather diluted, but we managed quite a few progressive changes. First it was stated that as soon as a member attains the age of 70 the class to which he belongs shall meet and suggest a successor. Further we succeeded in increasing the number of members of the classes for physics and chemistry, which have an important duty with the Nobel agenda. We also succeeded in enlarging the class for medicine. It previously had only fifteen members (below 70); now it was increased to eighteen. In order to provide a future president, someone experienced in the administration of the Academy, a second vice-president was introduced, the first vice-president always being chosen from previous presidents. This we proposed as we thought it necessary to strengthen the insight of the Presidium into the Academy's affairs, and to lighten the burden and responsibility of the permanent secretary.

The main income of the Academy has, since its inauguration in 1739, been the calendar privilege which today runs up to 4 million Crowns. The money was used to run all the important institutions; the Library, the Observatory of Stockholm, the Physical Station of Kiruna, the marine biological station at Kristineberg, the station at Abisko in Lapland and other scientific enterprises. In 1969 the Government decided to abolish this privilege. The Academy will thus in the near future have to send in its budget to the Government each year, like all other Government institutions. This will, of course, mean a great change in the administration, but it is difficult to say whether it will be better or worse for the Academy. It may, however, lead to more fundamental reorganization of the old Academy which may change some of its character but will still, I hope, retain the charming atmosphere of its meetings which is that of an old gentlemen's club.

CHAPTER XXIII

Brita's Uncle with Alfred Nobel in Paris, 1890-91. —
Nobel Committees at work. — Skåling at Swedish dinners.
— The Nobel Prize award ceremony. — The Nobel ban-
quet. — The King's dinner. — Sancta Lucia celebrations.

As Brita's uncle and governor, Professor Johan Erik Johansson
("Uncle Jöns"), was chairman of the Nobel Committee for Physiology and Medicine, at Karolinska Institutet, and one of his
sisters was married to Svante Arrhenius, the great physical chemist,
the first Swede to be awarded the prize for his ionic dissociation
theory in 1903, Brita and later on I were accustomed to meeting
the new Nobel laureates each year in December. Uncle Jöns had
long-standing connections with the great benefactor as could be
seen from the scientific correspondence which I inherited on his
death. When in 1890 he was working in an institute in Basle
in Switzerland, he received the following letter from one of his
friends and colleagues in Stockholm, Dr. Sven von Hofsten, head of
Samariten, a children's hospital in Stockholm. It runs:

Dear Friend,
    As you may have learnt from the newspapers, Ingénieur Alfred
Nobel in Paris has donated 50,000 Crowns to Karolinska Institutet to promote experimental research and 50,000 Crowns to the
New Lying-in Hospital of South Stockholm. During the negotiations I got to know the person in question and I had a most re-
freshing discussion with him for about one and a half hours. I
cannot recollect that I ever have met such an intelligent and
interesting person.
    On this occasion we also entered into physiological and biolo-
gical problems, which very actively occupied his inventive mind.

248

Professor Johan Erik Johansson, 1927.

He expressed his lively wish to get together with some young trained Swedish physiologist, with whom he might co-operate, or, to express it better, who might be capable of realizing some of the many – both original and congenial – ideas in the field of physiology, which were growing in his inventive head. I mentioned you and he asked me urgently to write to you and ask you to get in touch with him immediately.

The man is a bachelor domiciled in Paris and a multimillionaire; outside Paris he owns a villa where he has a complete laboratory which he will put at your disposal. I am sure that, if you like each other, *nothing* will fail. Write to him and tell him when you will arrive in Paris; make yourself familiar with his ideas etc. It may be that your coming together will prove valuable for you as well as for Swedish science. If I did not believe that you would profit in many ways from this acquaintance, I should not have suggested it. Give him my sincere greetings.

I hope that you are well and finding yourself at ease abroad. Paris is however *etwar anders* than Berlin. Live well.

Your faithful friend,
Sven von Hofsten.

This letter apparently reached Johansson in Basle. It has no date but Johansson has written on it with red pencil *St 13.9.90.* The dossier contains a telegram from Nobel to Johansson in Leipzig dated 30.9.90 which runs: "I will arrive in Paris within a few days and am looking forward with great pleasure to our meeting as promised – Nobel."

It is obvious that Johansson met Nobel in October in Paris. In a telegram from Nobel dated 30.10.90, Nobel regrets that his business hinders him from "wandering from the boring life of business into fantasy excursions in the fields we recently discussed" and says that he will soon return.

A later telegram of 11.11.90 runs: "Your friendly visit at any time of the day would be very dear to me."

After this telegram there is a bill dated 26.11.90 for a number of surgical instruments. On the back of this bill Johansson wrote: "For physiological exp. in Alfr. Nobel's laboratory, Sevran." Then follow two short letters dated 29.1.91 and 3.2.91 from G. Feuerbach, one of Nobel's associates in his laboratory in Sevran, in which he writes that he has not heard anything for a long time from Nobel. Then follows on 10.3.91 the following letter from Nobel.

Honoured Herr Doctor,
I am ashamed that I reply so late to your friendly letter, but as

it is the fault of the businessmen it should weigh on their consciences.

I had indeed realized that blood when outside the organism is very quickly changed, and for that reason I wanted to transfer it in the shortest possible distance and time. My belief is that it can be transferred, without any essential loss of the vitality of the blood corpuscles, through tubes drawn from melted fluor-sodium or sodium silicate. The walls of these tubes ought to inhibit the coagulation without changing corpuscles which come in direct contact with the walls. Similarly, it is feasible that the blood perhaps is modified ten times as much during the second second than during the first second.

Then come a few lines concerning Johansson's brother, mining engineer Per E. Johansson, about his eventual entry into one of Nobel's companies.

This is the only letter which contains something of wider interest. Johansson told me that Nobel offered to place him as head of a great laboratory in Paris for experimental research. Nobel was, however, so much occupied with business and his health was so poor, that he never had the opportunity to formulate his plans properly; so when Johansson received a message that he had been appointed reader in physiology at Karolinska Institutet he played safe and returned to Stockholm. He was the eldest of a large family of eleven sisters and brothers, who were more or less financially dependent on him.

Whether Johansson met Nobel later I do not know, but every New Year he received a greeting from him. The last one is dated San Remo 1896.

I often asked Uncle Jöns to write down his memories of Nobel in Paris, 1890–91, but it was never done.

It appears from Nobel's letter that he and Johansson were occupied with experiments on blood transfusion, which in those days gave the surgeons great difficulty. The problem was first solved in our time and in quite another way than Nobel and Johansson envisaged – with the discovery of the different blood groups.

In this connection it is thus worth mentioning that the most important discovery which led to the modern technique of blood transfusion was rewarded by the Nobel Foundation when the Vienna medical scientist Karl Landsteiner, later on professor at the Rockefeller Institute, was awarded the Nobel Prize in Physiology or Medicine for his discovery of man's different blood groups.

Perhaps you may be interested to know how the Nobel Committees work. There are five, each consisting of at least five members: The Committee for Physics and the Committee for Chemistry, whose members are elected by the classes of physics and chemistry of the Royal Swedish Academy of Science (K.V.A.); the Committee for Physiology and Medicine elected by the members of the Medical Faculty of Karolinska Institutet; the Committee for Literature elected by the eighteen members of the Swedish Academy; and the Peace Committee elected by the Norwegian Parliament, Stortinget. Dating from 1969, there is now another prize awarded in Stockholm with the other prizes, a "prize in Economic Sciences to the memory of Alfred Nobel", donated to the Nobel Foundation by the Central Bank of Sweden (Sveriges Riksbank). The "Peace Prize" is awarded by the Nobel Committee of Norway's Parliament, all the other prizes are presented in Stockholm on 10 December, the anniversary of the death of the great benefactor.

The examining and handling of the new prize are in the hands of a Prize Committee for Economic Sciences elected by the members of the Class X for Economic Sciences of our Academy of Science.

All these Nobel Committees send out every year confidential invitations to members of academies, university faculties and distinguished men of science or literature to nominate candidates for the different prizes. Such nominations, which are asked to be kept strictly confidential, together with a short citation, have to be sent to the respective Committees before 1 February.

The nominations are sorted by each Committee and in May a certain number which the Committee finds especially interesting are sent for closer examination to one or more specialists either within or outside the Committee. It may happen that specialists from abroad are called in to give their opinion. These special reports, often up to fifty pages, must be handed in to the Committee by the end of August. The Committees now meet and discuss the selected number of candidates. It is a hard task. How can you compare a discovery in cancer research with a discovery about, let us say, the function of the eye; or the discovery of a new rare elementary particle with the discovery of the special properties of semiconductors (which led to the use of transistors in our radios). But I believe it is generally thought by the world that the Committees have – with a few exceptions – done good work. Old Uncle Jöns used to say when we discussed it: "We can be happy that we have not made more mistakes. It could so easily have happened."

By the end of October the Committees have usually reached their decisions, which more often than not are unanimous, and they hand over their reports to the deciding body, the academies or the Medical Faculty of Karolinska Institutet. (How the examination is carried out in Norway, I do not know.) These bodies meet *in pleno* and discuss the candidates. Often there is very little discussion of the Committee's choice of candidates. The prize can be divided between two discoveries and cannot be awarded to more than three persons. It sometimes happens that half the prize is given to one candidate while the other half is shared by two.

It may happen, however, that the Committee's proposal is rejected by the executive bodies, i.e. the Faculty or the Academy elects another candidate; or, as once occurred, that the prize is awarded in spite of the wishes of the Committee not to award a prize that year.

Sometimes, but very rarely, it has been possible to award the prize for a discovery made during the previous year. That happened with Banting and Macleod for their discovery of insulin in 1923, but generally the discovery was made years back. Eijkman thus received his prize in 1929 for his discovery of vitamin B_1 in 1897. It is possible to do this as the wording in Nobel's will has been interpreted in the statutes to include in later years a discovery whose significance is not fully understood at first.

Swedish candidates are, of course, particularly severely scrutinized. After 1911, when Alvar Gullstrand received the prize for his work on the refraction of the eye, it was 44 years until another Swede, Hugo Theorell, received the prize in Physiology or Medicine in 1955 for his fundamental discovery in enzyme chemistry. He reported this first in 1935. Perhaps the Committee and Faculty of Karolinska Institutet feared that the Academy of Science would steal their famous scientist if they awarded him the prize in chemistry that year. For Ragnar Granit, professor of neurophysiology at Karolinska Institutet, it was also to take many years. He came to Stockholm in 1941 and published his papers concerning colour vision in 1943. He had to wait until 1967, when he shared the prize with George Wald of Harvard and Keffer Hartline of the Rockefeller University. At that time Granit had left the field of vision many years before and was doing important work on the control of muscular movements. If thus, for safety's sake, the Nobel Committees have had to disregard Alfred Nobel's will which states "for a discovery during the last year", they have, of course, had still more difficulties in interpreting his statement "for a discovery to the greatest benefit of mankind". Uncle Jöns, who was a great philosopher, often discussed this with me. He used to ask the rhetorical question: "Should you not give the discoverer of aspirin a preference over, let us say, Pavlov's discovery in digestion? Aspirin has obviously proved to be of greatest benefit and is perhaps the most used of all medicines." He continued: "The prize must of course be given for a high intellectual performance which leads to an important discovery; and in the word discovery is the intrinsic element of surprise. The scientific endeavour must result in a disclosure of something previously not understood or grasped quite independently from its immediate practical exploitation." *Il n'y a pas de science, que de science desinteresée,* said the great mathematician and politician, Henri Poincaré. "The Physiology of today is the Medicine of tomorrow," said Ernest Starling in his banquet speech of 1926 in Stockholm.

Any proper scientific discovery will sooner or later prove useful in human life. In this spirit the Nobel Committees have worked and will work in the future, independent as far as possible of the immediate practical or political applications. Opinions may be divided, just as tastes differ, but as a whole the scientific world has generally accepted the choice of the Swedish Nobel Committees. This is naturally the basis of the prizes being the most coveted in the world. They are today equally honoured by the East as in the West. It is only for short periods that a Nobel laureate has been forbidden to receive his prize. The first was Ossietzky, who was elected Peace Prize winner in 1936. He was then in a Nazi prison and Hitler, boiling with rage, declared that it was a disgrace and denounced the Nobel Foundation. Consequently Domagh, the discoverer of sulpha, and Butenandt, the great chemist, were not allowed to receive their awards. I saw the first letter from Domagh, where he, overwhelmed by happiness, wrote to the Nobel Committee expressing his gratitude. A few weeks later there arrived a second letter from him in which he denounced the prize – a position forced upon him by the Nazis. Both these German scientists, as well as the German physicist Otto Hahn (who made the discovery of the splitting of atoms, perhaps one of the most revolutionary contributions to physics) could never receive their prize money. After the war they were presented, however, with their gold medals and diplomas.

In 1958 the Russian writer Pasternak was elected for the prize in literature. For some time nothing was heard from Moscow. But then reports were published that the Russian writers' trade union were highly opposed to a prize to the author of *Dr. Zhivago*, the manuscript of which was smuggled out of Russia and first printed by an Italian publisher. The union raised an outcry and after a while it was said that Pasternak was forced to refuse the prize: he never came to Stockholm to collect it. I have a kind of feeling that the initiative in this was not taken by the political leaders headed by Kruschev, but that they had to give in to the rabid leaders of the writers' trade union, Pasternak's own colleagues, who begrudged him his award. Several years later I was astonished to listen to an after-dinner speech in the Town Hall by Solokov in which he denigrated the works of Pasternak. After the banquet I met Solokov down in the Blue Hall and asked him, through his interpreter, why he was so rude about his late colleague Pasternak. But Solokov only smiled and the interpreter never gave me an answer. How can I be sure that he translated my words properly?

The elected Nobel laureates with their wives, and often their entire families, arrive a few days before 10 December, the day of the award, which is also the date of Alfred Nobel's death at San Remo in 1896. It is the worst season of the year in Stockholm, snowing or raining, with occasionally a very pale sun rising a few tenths of a degree above the horizon, to descend again about 2.45 in the afternoon. The laureates are met by the Secretaries of the Nobel Committees; they are each provided with an aide-de-camp, a young secretary from the Foreign Office, who arranges transport and informs them about all the social events ahead. They are accommodated at the Grand Hotel at the North River, facing the

Keffer Hartline and Yngve Zotterman after dinner, 9 December 1967.

beautiful Royal Palace, the wonderful and imposing creation of Nikodemus Tessin, father and son, 1680–1720. Journalists and photographers swarm around them in the lobby, the newspapers print long interviews, the whole of Stockholm bids them a hearty welcome. Many of them have difficulty finding tails and accessories for the ceremony, and their wives in finding long evening gowns and getting their hair dressed. Their aide-de-camp presents them with a long list of social engagements.

Brita used to be very busy on these occasions. She worked from 9 a.m. to 5 p.m. in the lab, but she had one or two servants in the thirties who took care of the children and the household. But as quite a few scientists were elected whom we knew well, we often took the opportunity of inviting them for dinner at our apartment in town and later in our house at Experimentalfältet or finally at the Wenner-Gren Centre, where we now are living.

Ragnar Granit and Lord Adrian, 9 December 1967.

Brita generally laid the table for about eighteen people and saw
to it that the house was without a speck of dust – like her paternal
aunts, she is very meticulous, carefully planning each detail. A
good woman cook sometimes came the day before to prepare some
of the food, and then came early again next morning. At noon two
experienced waitresses arrived with their dark dresses, starched
aprons and white caps. They were given coffee and biscuits before
they started to fold the napkins, polish the silver, etc. When I
came home about 5 o'clock I found a busy household and Brita
with flushed cheeks and stage fright. I sat down to plan the
seating, writing the names of our guests on white place cards with
gilt edges; the guests had to be placed very carefully in order of
their social rank, as is the custom even today at such a party.

The first guests arrived very punctually at 7 o'clock. The waitresses helped them out of their heavy winter coats which were

258

neatly hung on hangers in the entrance hall. In a few minutes everybody had arrived, had received a drink and the noise level was steadily rising when suddenly a waitress would open the door to the dining-room and announce that dinner was served. As the host, I turned to the first lady of the party, bowed and offered her my arm and we entered the dining-room standing behind our chairs to wait for the other guests. The gentlemen had all received a card telling them who their lady partner was and their seats at the table. Finally, Brita, the hostess, arrived with the first guest of honour and we sat down. The table was an old oak table made in late Victorian style in the 1880s. It had belonged to Svante Arrhenius, the first Swedish Nobel Laureate (1903). I remember that George Wald (Nobel laureate, 1967) got very excited when, in my welcoming speech, I told our guests that "If this table could talk, or if there had been some kind of tape recorder hidden in it, you would have been able to listen to what was said by the earliest Nobel laureates, Roentgen, J. J. Thompson, Pavlov, Emil Fischer, Marie Curie, etc., who in the early days of our century dined at this very table a day or two before their award." Over the white table cloth of very best linen damask were beautiful flower decorations and shining silver candelabras carrying lighted candles.

We usually started with gratinated lobster or a fillet of sole either *au gratin* or grilled with a tasty sauce and always served with small boiled or mashed potatoes. With this first course we had a white wine from Rhine or Moselle.* The next course used to be some game like a roasted capercailzie, or a saddle of young reindeer with which we had a good Burgundy. As a dessert we often served an almond cake in thin crispy leaves like *mille*

---

*) It is an old Swedish custom that as soon as the first wine is served the host strikes the glass, asking attention for a short speech making the guests welcome to the table.

feuilles filled with either vanilla ice cream or a thick lemon cream. We drank to our guests in red port-wine.

Well, I ought to say a few words about our drinking habits at the table. At a Swedish dinner party it is the rule that the host first drinks to his lady partner. He lifts his glass to a position just below his collar and, with a slight bow of his head, he says *"Skål"* and smilingly looks in her eyes. Then he drinks, returns the glass to the first position and smiling, catching her eye again, he finally puts down his glass on the table. In military circles you lift your glass to the position of the third button of the military jacket.

The hostess first *skåls* with her partner – the gentleman on her left side, the "heart side". Then she, like the host, has to *skål* with all the guests in the order they are placed at the table. All the guests do the same, drinking to everybody. I was once reproached after dinner by a lady: "I say, you did not *skål* to me." When the table is laid for more than seven you must not *skål* with the host and hostess. They are supposed to be too busy *skåling* all their guests. Once an Englishman was told about these rules. When he, the next morning, was asked by his informant how he managed, he replied gaily: "I did very well, I believe; every time the hostess smiled at me I managed to look aside and avoid her *skåling.*"

When the dessert is eaten it is the duty of the guest who accompanies the hostess to the table (seated on her left side) to give a speech of thanks to her for preparing the meal and to the host for providing the wines. For many this is quite an ordeal which may even totally destroy the pleasure of the meal. For this reason in Brita's family the youngsters of both sexes had to take turns to give such a speech at every Sunday dinner. It was good and useful training. Once at the Nobel Institute of Chemistry, I was seated on the left side of the hostess, Brita's aunt Maja Arrhenius. It was not my lucky day. Being a medical man (this was in 1925) I was considered to be so familiar with anatomy and skilled in using a knife that I was trusted to cut the huge roastbeef at a sideboard. At first it went well, Brita carrying the slices on the plates to the guests, but suddenly the whole roast tipped over and fell on the floor. Tableau. I was saved by Brita's other aunt, Anna, who rushed to my aid, picked up the roastbeef and said: "Don't worry, we have another roastbeef in the kitchen." That was a white lie of course. In a few minutes she entered with the supposedly second roastbeef and cut it herself thus releasing me to try to find words for my after-dinner speech. I could not find any, so finally I rose and said: "I beg the guests to unite with me in drinking a toast of thanks to our hostess and host." After having risen from the table, all the guests shook hands with the hostess and host. I remember that Svante Arrhenius patted my shoulder and said with a sardonic smile: "That was an excellent speech; you must give it me in writing." He was always a great humorist.

Many after-dinner speakers relied on stories. One which was quite common was the story of the lion in Nero's circus. When a huge lion rushed into the arena a tall red-bearded Christian stepped aside and whispered something into its ear and the lion became very gloomy and left the scene of the sacrifices. Nero, who noticed this, ordered a man to ask the Christian what he had said. He refused to say. "Tell him that I will let him go free," said Nero. He still refused. "Tell him that I will let all the Christians in the arena free," finally promised the very curious Nero. The tall Christian then stepped up in front of Nero and said: "Great Caesar, I told the lion: You may readily eat me up but do not forget that you have to deliver the after dinner speech."

Another story which I sometimes have found very useful is about a Scotsman named Christie, who did not know that it was his duty to give a speech. On the other side of the hostess, how-ever, a Swedish gentleman, called Mr. Ameln, rose and said: "In Christie's name thanks for the dinner, Ameln."

The Nobel Award Ceremony.

Brita had attended this ceremony several times already in the second decade of the century. I saw it for the first time in 1920 when it still took place in the great hall of the Academy of Music at Nybroviken. From 1926 onwards it took place in the bigger hall of the new Concert Hall of Stockholm's Haymarket with the beautiful Orfeus fountain by Carl Milles to the left on the flight of steps leading up to the entrance. You have to take your seat in good time before the King and the Royal family arrive. The members of the awarding institutions are placed behind the pulpit on the platform decorated with flags and flowers, the floor is covered with a blue carpet with the three crowns of the coat of arms of Sweden. The members of the Government and the diplomatic corps, some dressed in beautiful national costumes and their ladies in colourful robes, are placed in the first rows of seats. It is a very elegant audience.

Suddenly there is a trumpet call. The tall King enters with members of the Royal family, nearly always among them is his cousin, Princess Margareta of Denmark, the eldest daughter of his late uncle Prince Carl and his Danish wife, Princess Ingeborg, the mother of two Queens, Astrid of Belgium and Märta of Norway, both dead. The King in civil evening dress wears the blue ribbon of the Serafimer Order and takes his seat when the orchestra has played the King's Song, which is sung by the standing audience.

Another trumpet call. The doors in the middle of the platform are opened, everybody rises again as the elected laureates enter, each conducted by the man who is to present his discovery or contribution to literature in a speech. They proceed to a semi-circle of chairs on the left side of the speaker's pulpit, the speakers take their places on the opposite side. The chairman of the Board of Directors of the Nobel Foundation now steps forward and gives a short oration for about 15 minutes, in Swedish, which many

The Nobel Prize award in the Concert Hall, 1950. Professor Liljestrand is ending his presentation and asks the three medical prize winners, Kendall, Reichstein and Hench, to step down to receive their gold medals, diplomas and cheques. (Photo: Herbert Hensel.)

The Royal family and members of the audience laughing as something unexpected happens. (Photograph by permission of Associated Press, London.)

of this very international audience do not understand. A booklet containing the speeches in different languages has, however, been prepared for them. The orchestra plays and the speaker who has to present the work of the elected laureate in physics enters the pulpit and reads his address, ending with a few words of congratulation from the Academy of Science in the laureate's own language. Finally, he asks him to step down the flight of stairs to receive the prize from the hands of His Majesty the King. A tall handsome gentleman, Dr. Arvid Hedelius, who has done this for 50 years, hands over the gold medal, the diploma and an envelope with an assignment of the prize (last year[1] it was for 350.000 Crowns) to the King who, shaking hands with the lucky

---

[1] in 1968.

George Wald receives his medal and diploma from King Gustaf
VI Adolf. (Photograph by permission of Associated Press,
London.)

man, congratulates him and bids him welcome to dinner at his
Palace the next night.

Some more music is played and the next speaker starts his
presentation for the chemistry prize. And so it goes on until finally
the literary laureate has received his prize. The audience rises
and sings with the orchestra the Swedish national anthem. This
ritual has been strictly observed every year as far as I can remem-

ber, at least for 50 years. Only once was there an incident which broke the ritual ceremony. When the King had taken his seat, the Chairman of the Board went up to deliver his opening speech before the elected laureates and their consorts had entered the platform. I was sitting close to him so I could have reached his tails and stopped him but I did not grasp the gravity of the situation. He went up to the Pulpit, took out his manuscript, bowed and started: "Your Majesty, Royal Highnesses, ladies and gentlemen," when the managing director of the Foundation rushed forward and told him to stop. Then the horns were blown and the procession entered the platform while the King and everybody were laughing heartily, much appreciating the pleasure of this little incident quite outside the protocol. But the poor chairman, a very orderly and ambitious fellow, became quite pale. He sat there motionless until he had to return to the pulpit and start again. I sat at the side of the former Chancellor of the Swedish universities, a member of the Social Democratic Party wearing the blue ribbon, the order of the Serafimer, who whispered in my ear with a characteristic twinkle in his eyes and a quick turn of his head: "He can dispense with the opening words of his speech at any rate." Later in the evening I heard Prince Bertil comforting the unhappy chairman by telling him how much everybody enjoyed the diversion created by his little lapse.

Once there was another incident well worth recording. The Italian inventor G. Natta was elected to the Prize of Chemistry in 1963. He suffered badly from Parkinson's disease and only with the greatest effort, and aided by his son, did he manage to reach his seat on the platform. When the speaker asked him to step down to the King, he nearly fell when he tried to get up from his chair. The King, although 81, grasped the situation and with his long legs went up the stairs two at a time and standing there on the platform, handed over the medal, etc., to the invalid laureate. The audience burst into prolonged applause.

The Nobel Banquet.

Outside the Concert Hall on the square a dozen buses wait to carry the banquet guests to the Town Hall at the Mälar Lake. In the buses you meet your friends and discuss the success of the speakers at the ceremony, and so on. At the Town Hall those seated at the long high table running for 150 feet along one side of the Golden Chamber enter by the big tower, leave their clothes and proceed up to the Prince's Gallery, decorated by the King's paternal uncle, Prince Eugen, a great painter. The other guests enter into the Blue Hall, ascend the big stairway and take their seats at the twenty tables running across the banqueting hall. A trumpet sounds, and everybody rises as the King and the laureates enter from the side and take their seats at the high table.

It is a wonderful sight to see all these elegant people in this gorgeous hall, the walls in golden mosaic, picturing on one wall a huge figure, the Mälar Queen, symbolizing Stockholm at the locks of the Mälar lake, with sky-scrapers from New York on one side and with Oriental temples on the other – West and East. On the other walls you find portraits of famous Swedish scientists like Linnaeus and Swedenborg and writers and poets like Stiernhjelm and Bellman, and Strindberg, Sancta Birgitta, etc.

When the fresh smoked salmon is served and French champagne with it, a trumpet sounds, and the King stands up and proposes "a silent skål to the memory of the great Donator, Alfred Nobel". After the dessert, at the coffee stage, there follows a line of speakers. In 1968 I was asked to deliver the banquet speech to the laureates. As it has to be printed in *Les Prix Nobel,* the year book of the Nobel Foundation, I had written it a few days before so I could enjoy the dinner and the company of a beautiful and charming young lady, Mrs. Browaldh, who was once the Swedish champion of figure skating. My duty was to address all the laureates separately and propose a toast. As all the laureates came from English

View of the Golden Hall in the Stockholm Town Hall where all prize winners and 800 guests had a gala dinner on Sunday evening after the Nobel Prize Award ceremony in the Concert Hall, 10 December 1967. (Photograph by permission of Pressens Bild, Stockholm.)

speaking countries except the Japanese writer, Kawabata, I spoke only English ending up with a few phrases in Japanese, as follows:

Your Majesty, Royal Highnesses, Ladies and Gentlemen.

A few days after the Nobel Feast in 1932 I was dining with two new Nobel Laureates, Sir Charles Scott Sherrington from Oxford and Edgar Douglas Adrian of Cambridge. Sherrington felt very sad that night, as he had just been told that one of his young co-workers had died of tuberculosis. He said: "It is disgusting that the tubercular bacillus, one of the very lowest of all creatures, should be able to destroy such a wonderfully organized being as man." – "Well, Sir," I said rather naively, "if we had not any infectious diseases we might not have had any medical research nor the physiology of today." "Oh," interrupted Adrian, "don't you think, Yngve, that human curiosity would have led us quite as far?"

The drive to know has not yet been properly defined in words, nor yet in mathematical formulae, but it exists in all fields of human endeavour, and certainly behind all the efforts of the outstanding men who today have received Alfred Nobel's prizes.

In long series of research and in their deep analyses of matter and of mind they have attained new knowledge, each step leading to the uncovering of fresh problems to be solved. To them, certainly, are applicable the lines written by Longfellow:

> *The heights by great men reached*
> *and kept*
> *Were not attained by sudden*
> *flight,*
> *But they, while their companions*
> *slept,*
> *Were toiling upward in the night.*

Dr. Alvarez.

It is a great pleasure to express our deep admiration for your wonderful achievements towards an understanding of the intrinsic nature of matter. It has been a thrilling story to read how you have elaborated the most ingenious methods and succeeded in discovering elementary particles whose life-length does not exceed a millionth of a billionth of a second, a great advance in our insight into the microcosm of the atom.

We extend to you our warmest congratulations on your Nobel Prize for Physics.

Dr. Onsager.

It has been said that you were far ahead of your time in the 1930s, just as Svante Arrhenius was, with his dissociation theory, in the 1880s. Arrhenius formulated the laws governing the reversible reactions while you have solved the problem of the irreversible chemical reactions. Apparently your discovery is of the same general import. It has already proved valuable in chemistry, but also in the biological sciences. It has even given us hope that it will help us to understand conduction in our nervous system.

We extend to you our warmest congratulations for your Nobel Prize on Chemistry.

It has always been a mystery how a single cell like the fertilized egg can contain and pass on all the information laid down and modified during millions of years. The three scientists, who to-day share the 1968 year's Nobel Prize in Physiology or Medicine, Dr. Holley, Dr. Khorana and Dr. Nirenberg have revealed this deep secret of life. Their deciphering of the genetic code has been praised as one of the greatest biological discoveries of this century.

We extend to you three gentlemen our warmest congratulations.

270

For everybody who has been to Kyoto and visited the beautiful detached gardens of the ancient Imperial Palaces in this ancient capital of Japan, Kawabata's book *Kyoto* is delightful reading, although very few of us are able to read the story in all the wealth of the Japanese characters and letters of the original version. It gives us the quiet, highly cultured atmosphere of a country of great traditions. We have all fallen in love with his heroine, Chieko, a prototype of all the fragrant beauty and loveliness of the Japanese women. I should like to meet her in one of Kyoto's wonderful gardens and say the only words I know in Japanese:

Atana wa kirei desu – you are beautiful!

Yasunari Kawabata.

We admire the exquisite artistry and sensibility which you have displayed in your deep analysis of the Japanese character. We offer you, the first Japanese writer to be awarded the Nobel Prize in Literature, our most sincere congratulations. *Kawabata-san, Omedeto gozal masu!*

Let us now, in accordance with our Swedish traditions, stand up and join in a toast for the Nobel Laureates of 1968.

Then come the laureates. Most of them speak only briefly, with thanks for the great honour, telling you that they are grateful to their teachers and associates. A few give longer speeches. Only laureates in literature speak for a long time, sometimes presenting a whole novel as Selma Lagerlöf once did, and touched everybody's heartstrings by talking to her late father in Heaven. Between the course the Stockholm Student Choir, a group of very good singers, enter the Golden Chamber carrying their white velvet student caps with a blue and yellow cockade on the brim. The conductor, the eternally youthful Einar Ralf, raises his hands and the choir give us a wonderful musical experience. Once the beauti-

Lord Bertram Russell addressing the students in the Town Hall after the Nobel banquet 1950. (Photo: Herbert Hensel.)

ful young opera singer Laila Andersson, in a Victorian dress and with long blonde curls, sang accompanied by the choir the old Swedish song "Seventeen years I believe I was", the song that made Kristina Nilsson (later Comtessa di Casa Miranda) Sweden's most famous nightingale, next to Jenny Lind. When they have finished their programme, generally three songs, they march out again singing the "Students' March", with words and music by Prince Gustaf, the brother of the King's great grandfather King Oscar I, who was the son of the French Marshal Jean Baptiste Bernadotte, the first Bernadotte King of Sweden.

After the coffee (with Cognac and liqueurs) we proceed out on the huge balcony over the Blue Hall where the King and his court take their place in the middle, watching the students' corps of Stockholm march up with their banners, their speaker addressing the Nobel laureates in a short speech followed by a few songs from the choir. One of the laureates addresses the students and then the dancing starts to the tune of Strauss's waltz, "The Blue Danube", and goes on until 1.30 in the morning. At that time the students proceed to their clubhouses to have a small snack – a hot dog, snaps and beer – and dance on until early morning, while the older ones go home in the snowy night or proceed to night-caps in private houses.

The next morning the Nobel lectures follow in different localities. Then the laureates give a review of their latest research, sometimes very fascinating lectures too, as, for instance, that of Georg von Békésy who started with about 30 minutes' introduction on how to look at art. He is a great collector of prehistoric art. When this came to the King's ears he was asked to spend half a day in the Royal Palace, the King showing him his own collection. It is said of our King Gustaf VI Adolf that if he was not born to be a king, he would have become a professor of classical archaeology. Another extraordinarily good Nobel lecture was, I must say, that of George Wald in 1967 on vision. He is a most engaging speaker. Perhaps he learnt from my friend, the late Professor Selig Hecht, his teacher in the physiology of vision.

On the following night the laureates with their wives are invited to dinner at 7.30 p.m. at the Royal Palace. There they step up to the second floor and the big banquet hall, decorated in white and thus called the "White Sea". All around the walls the Royal gardeners have placed white lilac and red Christmas flowers, a most stunning effect, not to speak of the beautiful smell of the lilac. The guests are received and entertained by the ladies and gentlemen of the Court until the King enters, followed by the Royal family. They proceed to shake hands with all their guests lining the walls. Then the doors are opened to Charles XIth Gallery, where a long, beautifully decorated table is laid for about ninety guests.

The food is superb. The menu is composed by Hovtraktör Tore Wretman, the excellent director of Operakällaren, Riche and Stall-mästaregården, three of the best restaurants in Stockholm. The wines are excellent. In 1967 we were, for example, served a claret, Cheval Blanc 1947, which was very much appreciated. Brita was seated between "God and Mammon" as my witty friend Hugo Theorell said, between the Archbishop of Sweden and Jacob Wallenberg, the famous banker. They both praised the wine, and pledged her. There are no speeches at this dinner. In 1967 when the Israeli poet Agnon received the literature prize there were a lot of conferences between the court people and the Israeli Embassy, as Agnon is very orthodox and only drinks Israeli wines. The court marshal finally said: "Then he must drink the King's wine." "Oh, no," protested the Israelis. "Don't you know what the King's wine is?" asked the marshal. "It is water." The King has not smoked or had any wine or liquor since he first married. When this reached the King's ears, he reproached the Court official, saying, "Agnon is my guest, he shall have whatever he wishes. Serve him Israeli wines."

On 12 December further Nobel lectures take place and the laureates also find time to visit colleagues and scientific institutes after luncheon. The ladies may even find time to shop for Christmas gifts for their children and relatives at home. Next morning,

Three Nobel laureates, Du Vigneaud, Chain and Theorell, celebrating Sancta Lucia in the author's office at Veterinärhögskolan, Stockholm, 1955.

on 13 December, they are wakened early by a knock on the door. In enters the Sancta Lucia of Stockholm, a very beautiful girl in a long white gown to her ankles carrying a crown of green lingonberry leaves with six lighted white candles on her head. She is followed by maidens also dressed in white, carrying coffee and the specially shaped "Lucia bread", flavoured by yellow saffron and with raisins scattered on the top. Another girl carries a plate with ginger nuts in the shape of hearts. They sing a Swedish folksong about Sancta Lucia, the Neapolitan song. This custom, which originated in Wermland and Gothenburg, has since I was a young boy spread to the whole of Sweden, every city electing its own "Lucia bride". At home our two daughters, Helena and Agneta, with Johan as their "star boy", acted in turns as Lucias as long as they lived with us. When I arrived to give my early lecture

275

on 13 December, the students used to rush in dressed in white nightshirts, and offer me coffee and "glögg", a hot punch which had made them rather hilarious early in the morning. That night there are very lively Lucia parties at the different student fraternities to which the laureates used to be invited.

One laureate, a poet, who was wakened at 6 o'clock in his hotel by the Lucia with her candles entering his bedroom believed he had died and had been brought to Heaven. It took them quite some time to explain, although he hardly believed it, that he was still in this world.

CHAPTER XXIV

San Michele and Josef Oliv.

One night while we waited for our *pizza* in *Gallo Bianco's* garden Josef Oliv told me about his acquaintance with Axel Munthe. He first met him in Rome. He was hitchhiking in Italy in 1930 and came down to Naples and visited Capri to see the Villa Caprile[1] on the southern slope of Anacapri. There he was told that the Swedish Queen, who had been ill for some time, had been moved to Rome; she was seriously ill and very weak. So Josef Oliv, being a journalist on the small provincial newspaper *Nya Värmlands Tidningen* at Karlstad, rushed to Rome. There he went to the Queen's residence[2]. At the inner door he met a valet who told him that the servants were strictly forbidden to talk to anybody about the Queen. As Oliv was standing there, a tall man – as tall as King Gustaf – came out. "I stood in his path and, as he was wearing dark glasses, he stumbled over me." "What do you want, man?" exclaimed Dr. Munthe, for this was who the tall gentleman was. "I am a journalist." "How dare you intrude like this? You must wait for the official court bulletin." "But the Swedish people are anxious to know about the health of their Queen," stuttered Oliv in his pure Småland dialect. "I gather you are from Småland," said Munthe in the same dialect. "Where do you live? Give me your address. Is there a telephone?" So Oliv gave him his address and said that he believed there was a telephone in the kitchen of the simple pension where he lived. He then went away and forgot all about it.

Then two days later at 3 o'clock his landlady cried, "Signor Oliv, there is a phone call for you." He rushed to the telephone

---

[1] The resort built for Queen Victoria of Sweden.
[2] Villa Svezia in Rome belonged to the Royal Family.

and heard Dr. Munthe's voice: "The Queen of Sweden has just died. I promised to tell you and I am doing so before I contact the Swedish Legation." Oliv tried to thank him but he had rung off.

Oliv sent a cable to his paper: "The Queen of Sweden died in Rome at 3 p.m." and thus became a star reporter. He was accepted as a staff writer with *Svenska Dagbladet,* Stockholm's biggest conservative morning paper.

We met Josef Oliv at supper with our friends Vilgot and Elsa Hammarling (Vilgot had returned from London where we had met frequently in 1926–7) and one night in 1932 I went with Oliv to see and review two American films which were showing at 7–9 and at 9–11 p.m. We went to the newspaper offices, where he handed in his reviews and then went to Artists' House restaurant where we had a late supper. While consuming a bottle of *chianti,* Josef told me about his first visit to Italy. As a young man he had sailed before the mast. He left the ship at Messina, and I must leave to him to tell of his adventures while hitchhiking in Italy and of how he was able without knowing any foreign language to keep up a conversation with a pretty Italian girl using musical terms only – he had made violins and was very interested in music. Thus he calmed down when the girl said: "piano, piano" but increased in boldness when she cried: "presto, presto."

In 1948 Axel Munthe made his last will, in which he gave *Villa San Michele* with its art treasure, its beautiful gardens and chapel and the top of the mountain above with the ancient castle *Barbarossa,* to the Swedish State, designating Josef Oliv as its warden. The Government, however, was not interested. They rejected the offer as they believed it would be a costly proposition. After Munthe's death at the Royal Palace early in 1949, Josef Oliv managed with the aid of Crown Prince Gustaf Adolf (our present King) to solve the problem by forming Axel Munthe's San Michele Foundation.

Josef Oliv, the Warden of Villa San Michele at Anacapri, after receiving the ensignia of Commander of the Royal Wasa Order from the Swedish Ambassador in Rome.

When he came to Anacapri in 1949 Josef Oliv found the property in terrible condition. The roofs were leaking, an inch of dust covered the interiors, the gardens were full of weeds and many of the pillars of the pergola were broken. How Josef Oliv was able to find money for the repairs you can learn from his own writing. He became Sweden's greatest beggar. Constructors, industrialists, and publishers all over Sweden were approached and many agreed to contribute.

In a few years Oliv was able to open San Michele to the public and receive Swedish visitors, composers, musicians, painters, writers and scientists in the different buildings.

Today more than 1000 tourists a day pay their small entrance fee to the museum where pretty young Swedish girls guide them through the beautiful house of Axel Munthe with its garden and its wonderful view down over Capri and the blue Gulf of Naples with Vesuvius and Naples in the far background. Apart from a modest grant from the Government at the outset this Swedish cultural outpost has been able by its own effort not only to support itself but has also been able to extend financial aid to the Swedish Institute in Rome.

Axel Munthe's intuition did not fail him when in his nineties he chose Josef Oliv, a son from his own Småland,[1] a cabinet maker, a poet, and a writer, to fulfil his last wishes and intentions for his beautiful Capri home. He could not have chosen a better man. When Josef Oliv resigned in 1968 after 20 years' devoted service, he could hand over to his successor, Consul Eric Berggren, a foundation in possession of more than twice as many buildings as in 1948, and a new beautiful pergola uniting the Foresteria and the Filippa, in which house Consul Berggren now has his office as well as a modern apartment for his growing family. And all this without any bank debts and a very sound economy. I take my hat off and bow deeply to Josef Oliv and his achievements.

Why has San Michele in Anacapri become such a tourist attraction? If you have read Munthe's book The Story of San Michele, which now appears in thirty-eight languages, you will understand. If you have not read it, you should. Then you will learn about a young fellow from Småland who studied medicine and qualified in Paris during the great days of Pasteur and Charcot, starting a practice as a gynæcologist first in Paris, and then in Rome. He certainly had learnt from the school of Charcot how to rule his women patients, among them the Queen of Sweden. He was active during an era in

---

[1]) Småland — small land in English.

which Western medicine slowly developed into natural science, but still was 80 per cent an art, and Munthe had all the qualities of a great artist.

To arrive on Capri by boat across the Gulf is a great pleasure. The anchor is cast in the port of Marina Grande and the boat backs in stern first to the quay. Dozens of hotel porters in their different liveries rush forward shouting the name of their hotels, offering their services. They are of no use to us as they refuse to help anybody who is not staying in their hotel, even though you offer them a large tip. Thus we always have to carry our heavy luggage more than 100 yards to waiting taxis, which bring us up the winding, narrow road through beautiful vineyards, first to the town of Capri, and then up the zigzag road on the steep rock a further 500 feet to Anacapri, the driver sounding the horn at each corner. He knows the road and where it is possible to pass other traffic. Sometimes, however, he has to stop and back down to a more suitable place in order to let a small bus pass. Halfway up he crosses himself when we pass the beautiful Madonna in a *niche* high up in the rock. On the crest of the rock one catches a glimpse of the upper part of the ancient *Phoenix* staircase leading to the Chapel of San Michele, which was the only access to Anacapri until 1912, when the present *strada* was cut in the rock.

One summer when we arrived a part of this *strada* had fallen down, so we had to go by motor boat to a jetty near the *Grotta Azzurra*. In rather heavy seas the able fishermen helped us ashore. Some ladies were very seasick, but these strong fellows managed to throw them ashore. For a whole week the motor traffic was held up between Capri and Anacapri.

Summers in Anacapri. — Our Emilia. — "La Perla." —
A beautiful Marchesa who loves jewellery.

A school of dolphins are tumbling in the deep blue waters 100 feet below, as we cross the Gulf of Naples. The pilot of our helicopter takes a short swing to follow them, dropping down to 30 feet. The graceful animals seem undisturbed. I can count forty three of them, diving and disporting in the waves. In a few minutes we shall approach the steep white limestone rocks of Capri. Will the helicopter be able to rise 1200 feet to land on the small landing strip at Damecuta? We circle round the German Solar Station, its white instrument tower rising up like the neck of a giraffe, and suddenly we are on the ground. Three taxi drivers rush towards us. Our old friend Benavente wins the race and in his open car with its fluttering sun shade, red and white striped like a Grännapolkagris, we climb the road which winds like a snake up to Anacapri. We find the main *strada* crowded with people. Quite a few wave to us: "Professore, Signora, benvenuto a Anacapri!" There is the blacksmith Massimino who makes beautiful wrought iron gates, our old friend Antonio of Piazza di Boffe, and there is Signorina Maria Vacca, one of three sisters who are our landladies at 21 Via Boffe.

"La strada è chiusa", says the driver. The procession is coming. The big wooden statue of St. Anthony bearing the Christ child in his arms is carried by six strong men. St. Anthony wears a tiara of small electric bulbs round his head, and is dressed like a Franciscan monk. From the balconies and windows red and yellow flowers (the broom is just in flower on the mountain) rain down on the saint and the picturesque *parocchi,* who is surrounded by his priests. With beautiful voices they chant their sacred songs as they solemnly walk in procession, while the rockets explode over the vineyards along their route, scaring away the evil spirits. They are followed by a group of citizens carrying white candles in their hands, and huge silver medals of St. Anthony round their necks. They are dressed in their dark suits – all handmade to measure (ready to wear men's clothes have not been introduced here yet). After them, preceded by a beautiful red and green banner, young maidens in white frocks walk singing, followed by small girls dressed in white lace with veils like brides; these are the confirmation girls taking their first communion, and looking exceedingly pretty; they carry white lilies in their hands. Next comes a group of small boys in brown monks' clothing each bearing a basket in which is a large loaf. A pretty nun helps them, and brings them into line again when they fall out of step. Most spectacular of all is, however, a little girl dressed in gold and scarlet with huge wings on her shoulders. She is exactly like the angel doll which slowly moves on a string tied from the roofs across the small Piazza di Boffe, to the great delight of all the small children.

As soon as the procession has passed, our dear friends the street sweepers Macelucci[1] the short and Salvatore the tall clear the street of all the flowers. The Sindaco (the mayor) Dr. Tommasso di Tommassi is a very firm and efficient magistrate. He not only keeps the city of Anacapri scrupulously clean, but he has also managed to give it two beautiful new roads – the winding road down to the grotta Azzurra and the new *strada* east of the central part of the city, thus relieving the main street, Strada Rolandi, from the heavier traffic which formerly nearly killed trade in the small bars and restaurants. The street noise became

---

[1] The tiny Macelucci is a great lover of wine. He is very chivalrous and always kisses Brita's hand very graciously.

When we meet him in a trattoria where he spends some time, he always generously offers us wine even at 8 o'clock in the morning as he quenches his thirst after many early hours of cleaning the streets.

Brita and Yngve Zotterman and Helena Cooley on the terrace in Anacapri.

unbearable to the customers. You will find the mayor walking along the main street in a spotless blue serge suit always looking very alert and carrying a little black bag containing his instruments – he is an obstetrician, and very busy as there is at least one child born each day in his district. He has given Anacapri a new *Scuola media* (grammar school) and a commercial high school which is housed in the beautiful Villa Rosa let to the city by Axel Munthe's San Michele Foundation.

From the main *piazza* of Anacapri runs the narrow street Via Boffe, named after General Boffe who was the governor of Capri during the Napoleonic era. It turns left into the tiny Piazza di Boffe with its small palm trees in the centre, and then winds down through the vineyards to the western side of the island. We live just behind the church of Santa Sofia; you can enter through a huge painted door, green against the whitewashed wall. You proceed through the house into a typical old Capriansian courtyard full of beautiful flower tubs, the purple flowers of *bougainvillea* covering the wall as high as our terrace on the first floor. Here we have lived for a month or two at a time during seven of the ten summers which we have spent in Anacapri. From this terrace we have a fine panoramic view east over the Monte Solaro, where the yellow broom blooms in June, spreading its sweet honey smell many hundreds of yards; in the south we look over the campagna, where the oaks, the olive trees and the Johannes bread trees give three different shades of green, and to the west we see a tiny strip of the Tyrrhenian Sea. We have our meals here on this terrace, on a round white marble table. I have written my reports here to the Nobel Committee and here we welcome our friends for supper when the moon is full.

The house belongs to an old family the *Vacca,* two old sisters Maria and Maddalena, who live on the ground floor; their elder brother Giovanno Vacca, who was a priest, died in 1968. The yard is full of rabbits and chicken. They own a large vineyard in the Boffe region, where they grow grapes, plums, cherries, figs, apples and pears. They make their own wine, red and white, in this yard, and have their own press for olive oil. It is wonderful to drink their natural rich wine and to use their oil, slightly greenish and smelling of olives. The house is not very comfortable. The beds are narrow and you lie in them almost as if in a hammock; water is scarce. There is only the rain water which they collect on the flat roofs in the rainy winter. Capri has no ground water. To supplement the rain water, which is collected in each property in a cisterna, often dating from Roman times, they are supplied by water from Naples shipped to the port *Marina Grande* and passed up to a huge cistern above the city.

One summer we thought we could live more comfortably so we took a double room with a bath in a hotel in the main street. It looked so attractive. But the street was noisy and the summer so extraordinarily hot that we slept very badly in the fine beds. We had no privacy and longed to be back in our old uncomfortable apartment with the nice old Vacca sisters. There we sleep well; sitting on the terrace in the sun and dressed only in my swimming trunks, I write these lines.

*   *   *

Domenico, my efficient barber, is cutting my hair. He does not use a machine, just a pair of scissors and a razor. It tickles as he cuts the small hairs on my neck with the tips of the scissors. At that moment Emilia walks down the main street of Anacapri. She wears a light turquoise blue frock over her little round body. She is 16 years old. When she notices me through the window she blows a kiss at me which I regret that I cannot return, as any quick jerk is contraindicated while Dominico shaves the hair border on my left temple.

Emilia passes by again; what is the matter? has she time to spare for walks? Emilia, our darling of this summer, our bonny child, is number five of a family with fourteen children. There should have been fifteen but one boy died. (Not because he was delicate, they are anxious to tell you, but from a ruptured appendix.)

The father, 50 years old, is *cantoniere provinciale,* that is, in the road police; a tiny fellow, rather shabbily dressed whether in uniform or in civilian clothes. During the war he met a beautiful Croatian girl at Trieste and brought her to Naples. They settled in Anacapri 7 years ago with ten children. They opened a restaurant, but could not get a licence for wine and beer. The wife baked *pizzas* which were collected from the shop and finally they obtained a licence. They rented a small bar in the main street and made the adjacent garden into a very nice *trattoria.* The situation was excellent, the pizzas made by the Croatian wife even more so, and people started to eat there, mostly labourers to begin with. The bar owner across the street tried to discredit

After a concert at Munthe's chapel, supper at Grottino's in Capri with Virginia Hutchings, the pianist.

them, suggesting that they used dangerous mineral oils in their cooking. Ada, the fourth child, a very sweet blondine, now aged 18 and working in an elegant store in Capri, drew many young customers.

This summer, however, we were greeted by her younger sister Emilia. She had already picked up so much Swedish from the young Swedes working at the solar station of our Academy of Science and at Villa S. Michele, that she greeted us in Swedish: "God afton, hur står det till" accompanied by a quick little curtsy, and when we left we both received smacking kisses on both cheeks.

This *Wunderkind* of grace and sweetness has become everybody's darling. Each evening the garden is full of customers. You see there many famous people, for instance the famous film producer Alberto Cavalcanti from Paris with his sculptured features and actors like Jean-Louis Phillip who is now recovering from his rôle as the college boy in "Tea and Sympathy" opposite

Ingrid Bergman for 2 years in Paris. There one sees the learned Dr. Holger Frykenstedt from Stockholm University, who is continuing his highly praised work on Ehrensvärd, the eighteenth century writer, painter and poet. The Swedish Consul, Erik Berggren, "Pierre", Josef Oliv's already very popular successor as the warden of San Michele, also sneaks in now and then.

How does she find time for everything, our Emilia? She works from 8 a.m. till 2 the morning. In the morning she tidies up the place, works in the laundry, serves at meal times and makes out the bills; she is helped by her 15-year-old brother Giovanni and sometimes at night by her brother-in-law, married to Enza who has a baby of 6 months whom Emilia often takes up in her lap when she is not nursing this baby's uncle, her own baby brother who is 3 months younger!

Last night when we had eaten our *pizza napolitana* Emilia went to our table and whispered in my ear: "I will serve you, Professore, with *coppa Olimpia speciale:* do not tell anybody," and she puts two fingers over her lips. We receive our favourite ice cream – vanilla with crumbs of black chocolate soaked in rum. It was immediately re-christened *Coppa Emilia.*

When on Sunday night the place is filled with customers Emilia places herself at a small table at the entrance of the bar and acts as cashier, letting the younger brother and sister do the serving. There she sits with a serene expression on her face, holding her pen and very conscious of the importance of her position. She is the only one in her family who can count properly. Her mother (aged 40) is an *analphabet.* "What is the use of reading and writing when you are cooking?" The schoolmasters recommended that the intelligent and talented Emilia should continue at school but the parents said no, they needed her in their restaurant "Gallo Bianco" (The White Cock).

While Anacapri's other eating places carry on with very little profit, "Gallo Bianco" receives a fair amount of customers not because they serve better food, and certainly not because their tablecloths are cleaner, but solely because the fifth child of the family, talented little Emilia, is there. She is not a striking beauty like her elder sister Ada; she has not an especially good figure either, but she has something much better: she has an exquisitely sweet personality, a joy in living which conquers everybody. You may sometimes have to wait an hour for your *pizza,* but Emilia always finds time to give you a few encouraging words: "It comes, it comes, *Professore Subito,* Mother will put extra much buffalo cheese, another ten minutes only, Professore."

We are all in love with Emilia.

*   *   *

"Take it," says the old lady, who keeps the jeweller's shop, fastening the clasp of a beautiful gold bracelet round Brita's wrist. "But I haven't the money," I say. "Never mind, you can pay next year." – "But I can't afford to buy such a very expensive thing." Her small peppercorn eyes scrutinize the label through her lorgnette. – "Well, I will give you a special price." She whispers in my ear an amount half that on the price ticket, making sure her daughters do not hear, of course. I cannot resist. She is a wily lady, this charming Italian jeweller, Olimpia Aprea, who started 50 years ago by selling tourist charms in Marina Grande, the small seaside village of Capri, and who now owns La Perla, a large jeweller's shop at the corner of the Piazza di Capri which every tourist has to pass. One of her pretty daughters has married a wealthy jeweller who sells most costly jewellery in his shop on the way to Quisisana, the only hotel de luxe in Capri. He is a fine, upstanding gentleman and has often helped me to get signet rings made for some of my friends. The best one was for Hugo Theorell on his sixtieth birthday. The monogram was designed by a fine Swedish artist, Göte Long, who was staying at San Michele that summer. The gold ring has the initials HT cut out on a small shield of gold which covers a rather large, rectangular blue lapis lazuli. Hugo Theorell usually wears it on his right hand when he plays the violin for his friends.

Beautiful Catarina Hagner, who for many years used to work for Josef Oliv in the San Michele Foundation, once told us a story about "La Perla", Signora Olimpia Aprea. A tourist bought a beautiful gold necklace from her, and after long haggling paid and left the shop. He had only gone a few steps when her two daughters ran out and stopped him, tears running down their cheeks. "Mamma is quite mad," they cried, "she is ruining us, she sells jewellery at less than wholesale prices." Whether she really did must remain a business secret. She died this spring and we miss this brave, gay lady: We always enjoyed sitting down at her desk for a long chat.

Last night we went in and bought a little gold ring set with small turquoises for our daughter Helena. At one of the desks a very distinguished-looking lady was talking to Lina, the elder daughter. "Where do you get the best food," I asked, "at Glauco, La Gemma or Grottini?" A long discussion followed in which the lady took part, speaking vivaciously in French while I did my best (which does not amount to much) to reply in that beautiful tongue, managing with a mixture of French and Italian. Finally we became very hungry so I asked the lady to come and have supper with us at Grottino. She looked at me; and Lina Federico nodded as if signifying that she could trust us, so she accepted. The lady, who turned out to come from Calabria, begged us to excuse her while she went into a shop – an electrician's – where she collected an electric kettle. "You see," she said, "I make my tea in my albergo each morning." We began to understand . . . . She was a poor widow trying to keep up appearances, like an old frigate flying the flag, by wearing beautiful and rather spectacular rings, the work of old Italian goldsmiths seldom seen in northern Europe.

We crossed the Piazza where the tourists sat, paying double

the price for everything they ate just for the privilege of seeing each other; we passed the crowd of youngsters sitting or standing on the steps to the church on one side of the street and the Palazzo Cerio, the ancient *palazzo reale* of the Neapolitan sovereigns on the other. It was here in the fourteenth century that the beautiful Queen Giovanna received Sancta Birgitta of Sweden and her son Karl who, instead of kissing her hand, embraced the Queen and kissed her on the lips which so enchanted the Queen that she made him her lover. His austere mother was very angry; in her letters she called the Queen a whore and prayed to God that they should be punished. And so they were; after 14 days of happiness Karl died of the plague in Naples. Queen Giovanna never forgot him, perhaps because she had had no time to become bored with him. She was generous in hospitality to his mother, who spent months in her palace, recovering from the strain of her pilgrimages to the Holy Land. St. Birgitta was no doubt also a great diplomat and certainly the most important and interesting person in Medieval Sweden.

"Professore è Signora," the gentle proprietor of Grottino greeted us. We were quickly given bread and a bottle of Vino di Caruso, a rosé wine from Ravello, though our Calabrian guest drank only mineral water. She talked unceasingly in both French and Italian. Brita, who at first had been rather suspicious, believing that the lady might be an adventuress, started to join in the conversation whenever there was a pause. Our guest told us that she had been widowed with three children after only 11 years of marriage. She had been born in Calabria, owned a palazzo and an estate there, a palazzo in Rome and another in Milan. She wrote down her Calabrian and Rome addresses for us. Brita still looked amused, as if she had heard it all before. When we had finished our first course (a gamberi, rice with fresh shrimps) the lady opened her handbag, took from it two small black velvet bags, undid the strings round them and emptied the contents out on to the white

Supper with the Marchesa at Grottino's in Capri.

tablecloth. What a sight: a wonderful necklace, an exquisite collar of gold in three shades, half an inch wide with a matching bracelet. She had bought them that night. I weighed them in my hands. "For heaven's sake", I said, "they must be worth quite a lot of money." She nodded "A million lire, Signor". Whether it was the wine or these beautiful specimens of a Neapolitan goldsmith's art which made Brita look complacent is difficult to tell.

After supper, our gentle guest said: "Now I should like to offer you coffee at the Piazza." So we went happily to the Piazza, looking forward to sitting there for an hour in the warm night with an espresso and a glass of Strega. "I do not like the draught," she said and took us into the bar. There, standing at the bar quite by ourselves, while waiters fetched their clients' orders, we had our coffee. It cost her only 150 lire (30 cents), one third of the normal price and without having to tip the waiter. I suppose that is how rich ladies who want to buy expensive jewellery live!

Next night Brita came down to the entrance of Villa San

292

Michele and cried: "Go up to the Chapel quickly, she has arrived and you must see her!" So I went up the lovely avenue of cypresses to Axel Munthe's Chapel and there on the terrace, the most beautiful foyer in the world, with its view over Capri and the Gulf of Naples, she stood, a goddess in a magnificent brocade coat, her auburn hair beautifully dressed, and wearing brilliant earrings. We entered the Chapel for Michael Steinberg's concert. She took off the coat she wore over her white gown revealing the exquisite gold necklace round her white neck, and around her wrist the matching bracelet. She was herself a jewel from top to toe. Our Swedish friends could not take their eyes off this brilliant bird of paradise among the sparrows. Her eyes glittered behind colossal light violet-coloured spectacles; she looked and behaved like a Queen. During the interval, as we smoked outside the Chapel, an old Italian lady approached her saying: "Marchesa, do you remember that we met in Rome last year in the house of ..." "Oh, yes Contessa," she replied. "I remember," – "So you are a Marchesa," I said. "Yes," she replied, "but I never introduce myself by that title."

The concert – Chopin's Preludes and Beethoven's Appassionata – was magnificent. Our young friend Michael Steinberg never played better, although the old grand piano (which was made by Malmsjö) was not in perfect condition. Michael had to put his left hand now and then on the string-damper in the basso to stop the continued sounding of the notes. We came out of the Chapel into the starlit southern night, quite bewildered with beauty, walked slowly to the Piazza Vittoria where I stopped a taxi to take the Marchesa to her hotel in the city of Capri 800 feet below.

Quite a few of our Swedish friends were eagerly practising their Italian and French on the Marchesa, who told them quite vehemently that she was annoyed because I stopped a taxi. She wanted to take an autobus! But how could I put a Queen in a mere autobus?